Our Miracle On The Mountain

Ruth N. Smith

ISBN 1-57087-016-0

Design Production by Robin Ober

Professional Press
Chapel Hill, North Carolina 27515-4371

Manufactured in the United States of America
96 95 94 93 92 10 9 8 7 6 5 4 3 2 1

Chapter 1

ROB

How do other men get involved with the other woman? The thought haunts me, and I wonder if it haunts them? Because I don't think many of us start off a new day thinking, "Today I'll cheat on my wife."

Rita! I inched her door closed without a sound and stepped warily across the gravel to my Malibu. Hunkering down behind the steering wheel, I slid my feet up over the brake pedal.

Fearfully, I lifted my arm to see the time - 3:30 Tuesday morning? Brother!

I pushed my head hard against the headrest, caught a breath, and leaned over to roll down the window and watch the stillness. Nothing moving out there but an old alley cat coming home from a hunt. It stung me. Just an old alley cat and me.

He walked sure-footed of his destiny, his right to prowl. Me? I was bent over and sick with torment. Because at night - I slide from my destiny - and move - into deceit.

No more. This has to end. Rita asked it again - "When will we get married?" I shuddered as I slumped over the wheel, because I knew what I had to do.

Just needed to sit here and inhale the lilac. Those mountains behind Spokane seemed to be hanging in the mists. It's a good earth ... I wanted to inhale it, reach out and embrace it. Who can take it all in, and not love life?

But this has been going on too long. I need to find out if I can do what I have to do. I've only been around twenty-three years.

Brother, that moon. What a moon ... but it haunts me. Because the moon always reminds me that I married Becky.

"Oh Becky, I can't watch that moon and not think of you. The prettiest girl in the class - you were that. And you wanted me." I closed my eyes and clenched my fists.

"How I loved you. Wanted to solve all your problems and because I loved you, I thought I must."

I looked up to scan the universe and spoke to it. "What a super old moon you've always been. Of all the times we sat together and watched you, Becky and I. Remember when Becky told me she was in trouble at home again and I told her, 'Don't cry, honey. We'll work it out.'"

"How I loved to dry her tears. Felt, if she let me carry her books, I should also carry her load."

I rearranged my head on the neck support. So much around for that last final glimpse. So much behind for that last backward glance.

"Remember, Old Moon, how we set up our do's and don'ts. We were trying to do what was right. Becky was, and so was I."

"No sex before we say I do. Right Rob? That's the way Jesus wants it. Marriage first ... OK?"

Wow! How we used to tear ourselves from each other's arms. The one time we didn't ... "Rob honey, I'm pregnant!" That's when marriage came fast.

Man, if a shake of the dice could just send me back to square one. We were happy then. So happy. My clenched fists socked each other. If I could just start over ...

"But, I've been cheating on you, Becky!" I cried. My head fell over the steering wheel. "There's too much water over the dam. I can't push it back! I can't push it back!" The truth exhausted me.

But I wasn't fighting myself tonight ... not like I had for months and months. What a piece of timing. To have gotten myself into a fix like this, just when things were looking up.

I rubbed the softness of my black leather pants. Never felt so smooth ... and the band ... had never sounded better than they did last night. For all our practicing, things were finally paying off. But I know what I have to do.

I turned the key and the motor answered with a quick start.

What a strange sort of calm this is. Like a crushing weight had been put on hold. It was quiet. Still. As though I'd given myself a weird bunch of peace and a small piece of time to live it.

Once again I wanted to inhale the rain washed lilac ... the new blooms on the night air were a sort of solace. They fostered a sense of well being that helped diffuse the chaos. Made me want to stay on and extend the spell. But I knew what I had to do and I had to do it right.

Suddenly my arms felt leaden and weary. Not tonight. Tomorrow.

There's wine in the back - enough to dull the torment. I turned the wheel and headed for home.

BECKY

Past noon and he isn't up yet! The clock kept jerking its hands around with a total indifference to the human havoc a day can make.

I wonder what time he got home last night? I can't watch his babies all day and then stay up half the night waiting for him.

Our marriage? ... with a Rita in it, it sure hasn't been too good. I held my temple hard. Would like to shake these thoughts. They simply handcuff all my efforts in everything I do.

Boy, and have I been getting the advice, whether I want it or not. Everybody seems to know what's going on and that really hurts.

Hard to hold your head up when your husband's cheating. When you've lost your husband to another woman, you blame yourself. And you're sure everyone else thinks there's a blame good reason for it.

I wiped the table and hung up new towels. My kitchen looked nice. The toaster sparkled. I admit I was pretty rotten at keeping house, but I've learned. More organized. Learned some things from Dr. Seuss, and they really worked. "Start in one corner and work your way around." Sure wish he had some answers for coping with the 'other woman'.

Rita! We carry insurance for every disaster - tornados, fires, or getting hit by a Mack Truck, but something like a Rita can wipe out every dream. And there's no reparation. Our lives can be shattered, both mine and the girls.

She's worse than a disaster.

"Dear me, that cat dish looks like it hasn't been washed in a month. Always something that I don't get done. Yesterday's jobs leave me so tired." I brushed the hair back from my face and caught a deep breath, which didn't seem to help.

I'm not expected to fight down a tornado so wouldn't feel guilty if it did me in. But I'm expected to out-battle Rita.

"Oops, didn't I take the hamburger out to thaw this morning either? Oh boy, that freezer needs defrosting ..." I tossed the meat in the sink.

'The other woman doesn't stand a chance if a man is happy at home.' That's what I've read and that's what they tell me. Hogwash! Just because I stay home and raise his babies while she's down there boozing it up with him!

"Oh, look at those ants! No matter what I do, they keep crawling around the sink faucet."

She told him he was better than Elvis. I never thought to tell him that. What does he see in her anyway? Honestly, I thought she didn't have a chance. At least I'd lost weight after Tasha came. Wanted to look as good as I could. The bread-box tossed back a rather lackluster image. A bit of lipstick could help. And if I brushed my hair it might help.

"I don't think Rita worries a whit about how she looks. Just angles up to him with that, 'How's Elvis to-night?'"

Now she's got me talking to myself again. Took a smack at the counter. What good did that do? Opened the screen and kicked the cat dish out. I'd get at it.

Leaned against the door and scanned our pretty yard. There was no joy out there either. Like my rhododendron that cascaded over the rocks. It had always been a springtime surprise to see how it would develop its blossoms ... or spotting Anja's favorite ball that had rolled under her wagon. They were both left where we played with them yesterday. I tried to remember her explosive little laughs and her gleeful gurgles that had her tumbling after her red ball when it slipped through her fingers.

The torment of what I knew I was losing tore up all joy. Tore up everything that tried to penetrate a heart that was taking a licking.

Chapter 2

ROB

The basement - I got a date down there. Got to get to that basement. I cuffed my head. It felt like mush. Boy, that wine sure worked. Thank goodness for that.

Becky? - she's in the kitchen, but I can't face her. Afraid to face her - 'fraid of those eyes. And the kids. I'm afraid of their eyes too. But to live - I'd hurt them more.

I looked at the stairs and paused only for that deep breath. The impetus I needed before the plunge.

"Oh Becky, I've always had your beauty on my inward eye. Golden curls that fall around a pretty face. And your skin - that creamy white skin! You'll always turn heads.

"I've been plunging to a white-out for so long and I've been grabbing for every twig along the way - not to stop me - just to delay. I can't do that anymore - not even to give you one more hug."

And after Rita again last night. I know what I have to do.

I started down. My legs felt spongy! I grabbed for the rail.

"Oh Lord, what went wrong? I meant it, really

meant it at the altar when I cried for your salvation. The peace, the joy, what happened? I wanted to sing. I wanted to do right by Becky.

"I tried to give her the house she wanted." I glanced back at the French Provincial doors. "That's what she wanted and that's what we built."

The last look. Everywhere I look it's the last look. Brother, she sure fixed it up. The deacon's bench stacked with her blue pillows. That lacy valance over the dining room drapes - first thing people see. I wanted a home my girls would be proud of when they ask their friends, "Want to sleep at my place tonight?"

I pulled at the rail and hung over it - if I could just blot it out - if I could just blot it out. If I could just start over. But too much has been frozen into an unforgiving past.

Rita - what did I see in her anyway? If she was pretty I could have put up my defenses. I just know I missed her when she wasn't in her corner. It was easier to sing when she was there. Applauding. Laughing at my jokes. So easy going, no fuss, she just went with the flow. Made me feel I was better than Elvis. Made me feel the world was waiting for my voice.

I pushed my way into the basement. Messy. I hated to leave a mess. Music sheets lay in piles. I straightened them. My old drums filled the west corner. I lined them up too. A last tribute. To what? A man condemned by his own deceit?

I straightened the old poster that I'd framed. Our old Heirborn Band! Brother! We sounded great when we sang at the fair for Jesus Northwest in Vancouver. Saw my reflection, and Man have I changed. I do look bad. Young - but an empty guilty image looked back. Empty because I had known a better joy. The others - what have they done with their lives? I couldn't stomach the thought. I only wanted to blot it out.

Memories. I shuddered and tried to forget them, but they just came searing back. Must I relive them? Must I justify what I can't rectify? I sagged into my leather chair.

Music, was that my downfall? Music always seemed my best ace in the hole. I looked at the laundry tubs that held everything but answers.

What I've done I did with music. Bought a home for Becky and the girls. Fixed it up. Paid bills.

When we got together, the guys and I, and formed this band, we sure had high hopes. I kept tracing doughnuts on my old drums. Like the baby shoes from your first steps, I wanted to preserve my drums.

Boy, did it seem great to get that job at the bar! We'd play the rock, but we were going to let them see Christ in our lives. A LIGHT IN A DARK PLACE. That was us. In a bar, that was where a light was needed. That's what we kept telling each other.

"Was it the drinks?" I was hunched over from the weight of my thoughts and I heard my voice like an echo.

"Come on boys, the drinks are on the house. Just drink a little so the customers will drink." I dropped my head and my body tightened. I couldn't take the booze! Maybe if I'd been brought up with it, but I wasn't. That's how it got me hooked. And it deadened my conscience.

"That was the start of Rita," I cried. "That was the start of Rita."

My grip shook the arms of my chair. I could find no voice to say it. "The drinks sure went down easy when Rita drank with me. In her eyes I was a winner. There's no struggle with her. Would life be easier with Rita?" My inner accusing poured ice on my spirit. I shivered. I shook.

"It's terribly alone down here." I shuddered and the sweat began trickling down my back. I wiped my face with my sleeve. Boy, my hair had grown. I pushed it back.

"Debts - over my head. Promises I've made that I can never keep - to Becky and to Rita too. The little girls, who laugh and reach for me when I come home - reach for a daddy who is a cheat. A liar.

If I just get out ... they'll all forget.

"Pills? That's a cowards way out. Like I wanted a high before calling it quits." I kept talking.

"Hanging - ? That's the worst way I can think of. That's the only way to go. No one could question my intention. More fitting for the mess I've made." I looked around and studied the mesh of wires under the laundry tubs. I'd find a way somehow. I'd find a way. It was as though I could hear a low drum roll begin in my head.

I pulled at my belt. "My belt!" I could hardly form the words. "I could do it with my belt."

My belt slipped easily into a noose around my neck. I'd found the way. The drums grew louder.

At last I was in control. I'd never hurt anyone again. I followed the support girder.

"There is a nail - that will do it!"

I pulled up a chair and climbed on it. Slipped the belt hole over the nail.

Drums were going faster, louder. I was doing it - whatever is ahead I deserve —

"Will you believe I tried, Mom?"

"Becky, I tried! Please forgive me —"

I kicked the chair away. The drums stopped—

BECKY

He did it again. Walked right downstairs! Wonder if he knows I live here? Why doesn't he just peek in, wave, say something. The jab I get when he heads for those stairs ... I don't know if it is from hurt or disgust.

I threw an arm over the towel rack and cradled my head. Women always knew what to do in the old movies. Cook better, look better. And their man always came back. Now ... they're all mixed up, like me ... because nothing seems to work.

"Well, he just mutilated my good intentions." I reached over and turned off the oven. I had mixed up some blueberry muffins because he liked them. The girls were still napping. Thought it would be fun to share some blueberry muffins together. But when he headed for that basement without so much as a wave, he sure turned off that intention.

Couldn't turn off the indignity of it all. He walked downstairs without even a, "Hi honey."

Wish I hadn't hit him. But at times like this I almost wished I'd hit him harder ... When he told me he wanted to marry Rita, I hit him. "How could he look in my eyes and tell me he didn't love me. That he wanted to marry that woman." I was talking to myself again.

Cheating! When I think of them together ... I just die. "Get your life in order before the Lord," Dad told me. "You can change yourself - you can't change Rob." It crumpled me like a fighter going down for the count. It doubled me.

"I should change? I should try harder? If they knew? People who tell me what to do! If they only knew. That when I try so hard he just ups and heads for the basement without even a wave."

But maybe Dad was right. If I could just have gotten my life together before the Lord. If we both could be like we used to be. How have we ever fallen away like we have? He used to be so wonderful.

"I want to save my marriage!" I cried. "I want him back. I've always wanted him. In junior high I knew I'd never love anybody else. I want to sing with him like we used to sing. I love him. Oh God, I love him!"

Thud —

"What was that? I ran to the basement stairs. It sounded like somebody fell. "Rob honey, are you alright?"

It was so quiet ... still.

"Rob!" I screamed. "Answer me!"

I clung to the rail to get down the steps. My knees felt weak. My arms cold. My eyes moved in slow motion for I was gripped with a foreboding that scarcely let me breathe.

That crumpled mound was Rob! "Oh God," I screamed. "Is it over?" I saw the broken belt tight around his neck.

I had no control of my screams. "Is it too late ... is it too late for us now?"

His face had fallen into a pool of froth and blood. My screams became my prayers. "Is it too late? ... is it too late for us now?"

The belt was cutting into his neck! I must loosen it! It was cutting off his life.

I shrieked for help. I tugged at the buckle to loosen it. Did he break his neck? I shouldn't shake him like this

... but he must breathe!

He was getting darker and darker; his lips were swelling. His tongue was filling his mouth. I loosened the noose. His body convulsed. He inhaled.

It was a struggle for life. He began doing what we take for granted with every breath we breathe.

I must call a doctor. I was still screaming. "Randy! His brother, Randy - he's a doctor!" I'll call his brother. He'll come. He'll know what to do. He'll take charge.

I called his mother. She was coming. "Go! Go back!" she ordered. "Go back to him. I'm on my way!"

The house filled with people, running and shouting orders. Rob was hysterical. He had gotten to his knees and locked himself in the bathroom.

"This is as bad as life gets, Lord." I cried to God for I was alone. Others had taken over.

But no, I realized, he was breathing. He was alive. We came so near a closure. So close to having had everything between us aborted by one more instant of time.

Strange to feel happy that what we had left to us were problems.

I had an idea, and it felt as though a compass was changing our course. An idea that blocked out what had happened because I saw a way for us.

"You really meant business this time Rob." Randy had finished his exam and was holding up one end of the belt that looked like it had been sliced by a razor. "Not many get a second chance like this."

He talked about committing him to a psychiatric ward. But he looked at Rob and me and he knew we had things that needed to be said to each other.

"I don't think you'll try something like this again." He patted him on the back and gave me a hug. "I'm just around the corner, Sis," he said as he left. Rob's brother always called me 'Sis' when it counted.

We sat together on the couch and held hands. I had never noticed how warm his hand was. I had never noticed breathing. It was strong and good. This was the time to say it.

"Rob honey. Do you remember how you wanted to go live on a mountain? Alone with God, just you and me? See what God could do with us?"

I waited for his answer. I could tell he was thinking.

Finally, he said it. "On a mountain?"

Chapter 3

ROB

A mountain top? I rolled it around. I pondered it. Long after the house had cleared of family and neighbors I lay listening to life sounds - a toilet flushing, short steps running through the hall, even the breathing sounds of my sleeping family. It meant waking to another day. Greeting a morning with, "Glad you're here." To feel like shouting, "It's another chance at living."

Little things like a created something hitting our screen made marvelous sounds. A spring sprinkle of rain that grew heavy enough to run down our gutters and splash on the stones - I relished the sound of it.

But the bottle - the wine that tingles and enlivens, I craved it. I wanted it. What would it take to rid the nerve cells of my soul of this terrible hunger? I have to overcome the pull to a bottle for a fix. Totally. Forever. Less than that means nothing. What we do in an instant of time takes a lifetime to undue. A lifetime to regret.

And the exhilaration of applause, that's a pull that's as bad as alcohol. All I had to do was overcome. Overcome the pull of a laughing, backslapping crowd that takes no stand for anything but themselves. Of being the somebody people talked about, came back to hear. I knew my addiction.

"But, oh Lord, how do I deal with Rita? How do I deal with that sin, so I will not sin again? Can You wipe her out of my mind? Wipe her out so I won't think of her? Her laughs - I must forget them. Help me make it up to Becky. The hurts. The tears. Oh God, how I've torn her heart apart.

"Oh wretched man that I am. The thing I would not do, that I do." I remembered the verse I had learned before the meaning of it became a part of the loathing of myself.

I slipped out of bed and dragged my stool to the window. The same old mist was whirling around the street light like it always had when the night was heavy with soft raindrops.

The magic of this life was out there ... still. And it wasn't wasted on me. My mind cleared - I was thinking better. Yes, I was thinking better. I thanked God again and again that the strap broke. "Oh Lord, is there grace enough for me?"

Becky's suggestion of a mountain top? ... at least I would be up there with the struggle of living. When I realized the 'tangled web' that had ensnared me. What could have tricked me into thinking it would be a sort of noble act to bow out of life? That it would be better for my family if the world didn't have me in it?

How close I came to destroying them. Saddling my children with the shame of suicide. Knowing their Daddy copped out, didn't have the courage to dig in and battle it out by living. By finding the strength in Jesus Christ to find victory, to overcome.

It would be painful for them to say that Daddy

died in an accident, or from cancer. But how could they form the words to admit that their Daddy hung himself in the basement.

My sense of decency and responsibility was wrung by the thoughts that wouldn't leave me. "I wasn't thinking of them, Lord. I've learned that. Nor was I thinking of Becky. I was thinking only of myself."

"On that mountain I can't fix my life with patches, Lord. The new creation has to be restored. Renew a conscience within me. Break the chains of my bondage - link by link, Oh, Lord Jesus. Whatever it takes. Do Your work Lord. Do Your work."

I thought of another seeker after truth who left words so strong that I memorized them as a kid, and they challenged me now. "I do not want to live life what is not life," said Thoreau, "I want to suck the marrow of life - if it's mean, let me prove its meanness, if it hurts then let me hurt." I drew from the thought as I prayed to God.

"Show me the marrow of Christianity, Lord. If it hurts, then let me hurt. I don't want to play church, oh God. I want holiness.

Chapter 4

BECKY

We would escape. Rob had talked about living on a mountain since we were kids in high school. "I'd really like to be a mountain man," he'd tell me when we were watching the moon. "Get up there close to God ..."

Now we were fleeing up there - to a mountain where the pull of sin would loose its grip. Where the battle of a soul, struggling with a force so evil that it could make a man destroy himself, would be safer to fight. We had to overcome.

If I feared what I was exchanging in order to save my marriage, the broken belt would always remind me of what I'd gained. I was ready to leave.

Rob found the ad the first time he looked. I had learned that whenever Rob had a problem, he'd look first in the want ads. And it was there he found our mountain, tucked in *The Spokane Review.* It sounded right.

"Becky, look here. I can't believe this. Ten acres! On a mountain! Electricity!"

His shelves were loaded with books about living off the land. Someone had written a book about making it on five acres. This was ten. Rob scrunched the paper as he folded it with the ad centered over the folds. "I can't believe this!" He waved it like it was a winning ticket.

"Let's go. Let's go. I tossed the towel and ran for the girls. We piled in the car. The mountain didn't tug at me as much as it did Rob. A glance at our French Provincial doors convinced me that saving our marriage had become a passion that obliterated every other concern. Up there, we could save our marriage. We had found a way. I felt it.

"It's only a couple hours drive, Becky. The days are getting longer. We'll have time." We were in the car for take off.

He pulled up to the Fhurmans Feed Store. "What are you stopping for, Rob?"

Already a bit of the glow that always sparked Rob's eyes had returned. He snapped the A-OK at me with his circled fingers and dashed in the store. Almost as quickly, he dashed out, flung a sack of potatoes in the back seat and handed me a bag filled with slippery packets.

"Seeds? Rob honey, you aren't just a bit eager, are you?" I thought of the verse, *"Behold, the Lord thy God has set the land before thee. Go up and possess it."* But I didn't really dare to claim it. This was unfolding too easily.

The hour and a half ride seemed short; the girls slept most of the way. Spring announced her presence in every breeze. All over, there was the fragrance of blossoms. The birds were reeling off their best mating calls and with the windows down, we could share them as we passed.

But finding the driveway to our land was not easy. No real estate man offered to drive us out there. He just gave us a bunch of directions that Rob wrote down on the side of the ad. When Rob handed the directions to me, deciphering them was almost as difficult as finding anything that resembled a drive. The grass and weeds waved on both sides of the road like a no trespassing sign - a bramble barrier defying even the most venturesome.

Just as we were driving past, we thought we spotted something that may have been a cow path and did a U-ie. Nothing else looked more favorable.

"That can't be it, Rob! Doesn't look like a cowboy could break path through that brush." We drove by again and circled back.

"Here's a farmhouse, Becky," Rob said, and swung into their drive. "With all that beef running around out there, I'll bet they've been around a long time and know every trail in these parts."

A farmer who fit the countryside picture, overalls and all, strode up to the car looking rather skeptical. Apparently strangers didn't barge in like we just did.

"Yeah?" he asked as he reset his hat.

"We're trying to find this place." Rob showed him the ad and read the directions he had scribbled on the side.

"Yeah, well that seems to fit the territory alright, but I don't know anything about there being a house up there."

"Well, we'll try it and see." Rob wasn't discouraged.

"By the way, I'm Brad," said our new neighbor as he extended his hand. "Are you guys planning on homesteading up there or something? Part of that 'back-to-the-land' thing I've been reading about?"

"Kind of." Rob nodded as he revved the motor.

"All I can say is, I wish you luck." I thought he was sizing up my fingernails as we drove off.

We tried the path, and it proved to be a road that we could follow. We wove back and forth through the trees

- up, up, up. The two miles seemed endless. Neither of us said a word.

We found it. Found a clearing; it was the struggle of someone who had begun holding off the wilderness. The grass was long and spindly, as though it had reached as high as it could for sunlight. Enough to make it. I noticed that. I sized up the potential.

The verse ... *if God be for you, who can be against you*, seemed to come with the package. It powered my feet.

We ran around the acreage, each holding a baby. The pine had spread a pungent essence that hung above us, as our tonic for coming. We were alone up here. I had never felt such a walled-in aloneness. It had a wonderful welcome feel, like the pull and drag of what we left behind could never reach us again.

"Becky, I feel this is it!" Rob shouted.

"So do I, Rob."

Everywhere there were trees. Pine trees. Trees that had left enough space between them so we could twirl around them and walk among them. I remembered the Bible Camps I had attended and the awesome awareness of God that I had sensed. There was that same awareness bound up in this wilderness that was claiming us totally.

"We will plant our seeds, Becky," Rob said solemnly.

"But, honey, we haven't even bought it yet."

"But we will, Becky."

"I know we will. I feel this is it, too, Rob honey."

We pulled out our spades and rakes from the trunk. As Rob dug, I ran for the packets I had in the glove compartment. Almost as a ceremony, we planted them. If we would live off the earth, we must give it seeds. We were claiming our soil.

From our hill, we looked over Chewelah, a town that seemed so friendly we could almost see their welcome mats. I wanted to claim them as my neighbors and friends.

We hadn't seen our house yet, and it didn't seem to matter. Up here we could shake off the crushing smog of sin and heal our marriage. We came prepared to cope and followed the road around the curves until Rob jammed on the brakes.

"Becky ... Look! Look! Look at that water gurgling right out of the mountain. That's a spring, Becky. Doesn't that look like the western movies we've seen?"

He stopped the car and ran to cup his hand under the hose that someone had pushed into the mountain to catch this crystal stream.

"It's cold! Wonderful! It tastes good!"

I knew it would have to be carried. I'd never carried a bucket of water, but others had. It was a thought that I would return to often. If others could do it - I could too. Now I was ready to see the house.

The road wove on for what seemed a long way to carry a bucket of water, and I wasn't at all prepared for what we saw.

"Whoever - would - build - something - like - that?" I gasped.

It wasn't the brownish grey, weathered old logs. And it wasn't the three foot stilts it seemed to balance on. It was all the old straw that had been packed underneath it.

"Straw! Rob! I can't live in a straw house! You know what happened to the little pig that lived in a straw house! No! No! Honey, I just can't do that," I cried.

Had we made a mistake?

ROB

I watched as the spirit and spark of my wife became replaced by second thoughts. Apprehension bathed her face. Was she buckling to the reality of where this venture might lead us? She wanted the feel of the forest up here, the aloneness with God. Did her nest make such a difference?

The cabin didn't confound me. "Becky, I can fix up that little place," I tried to assure her. "It's on stilts because the snow is so high up here in the winter that it would cover the windows. This way we'll be on top the snow. And the straw is for warmth so the wind won't blow under it."

"I can fix it up!" That little cabin had become the fulcrum of a life direction. The chance to flee the pull of a life that had almost destroyed me had met its snag.

"I can fix it up, honey." I could feel the wind tossing my hair as I made that promise.

"Oh." Becky nodded her understanding.

"All we need is money for the down payment -- and we can raise that. $15,000 for ten acres, Becky, that's not bad. All we need is the $1,500 for the down payment."

We bonded together in the euphoria of a new try at life. This was it! This was it! We reached for each other and our covenant was bound by each other's arms. No burning bush or parting waters could have made God's way seem more real. Suddenly time was our greatest asset.

"Let's get home and start raising all that money, Rob."

"Sure thing!" I said at last. "But give me one more minute with the garden." I raked it even and placed the markers, tossed the spades and rakes back in the trunk, hopped in, and started the motor. We would raise the money.

June days in Eastern Washington are some of the most predictable of the year for a yard sale. Even if they started cloudy the day would clear. We had to begin raising the $1,500.00 so we would start with selling our earthly possessions. They covered our yard, and we tried to remember modern ploys for bringing top dollar for each of them.

"Here, let's make a living room setting out of these," I said and piggy-backed our pull-up chairs and placed the magazine rack between them.

We could only take with us what would fit on the flatbed of the old '72 Chevie pick-up that we bought for $75.00 on a promise to pay.

Becky's beautiful couch was one thing that couldn't go. Neither could our bed.

"Most important are my tools, Becky," I told her. "If we're going to make it on that mountain, we'd better have tools. We can't do it with our teeth."

Chapter 5

BECKY

Our things brought $1,750.00. Rob paid off the truck and we signed the contract for the land.

"No one has answered our ad on the house, Rob. What are we going to do if it doesn't sell?"

"I've been thinking about that."

I'd been thinking about that too. I wanted to flee Spokane. I wanted to flee the house. Our basement episode was still raw in my thinking. We didn't talk about it. We couldn't. We both seemed to be functioning on an untried edge of hope that on that mountain we could put it all together again. We could find God's ways and save our marriage. We only had to get up there.

"We've improved the place a lot, Becky. I've been thinking that we might just turn the keys back to the mortgage company."

I was going to ask him what our folks might say about that. But I didn't. They knew the significance of the broken belt.

Perhaps it was the quiver and flush of adventure that helped ease the pain of parting with what we had begun together.

"Good idea, Rob honey. Houses aren't selling these days."

Our truck was groaning from its load even though all we took with us was our range, refrigerator, table and chairs, clothing and kitchenware.

And Rob's books. "Rob honey," I asked him, "how can we possibly take these books? I thought you'd at least be selling some of them at the sale."

"Becky, I've been collecting them since I started to read. I've almost memorized Thoreau. It would be like losing a leg to leave him behind. And my Harvard Classics? Honey, I can stick them around and under our things. They'll kind of act like packing." We took his books.

My greatest loss seemed to be my beautiful couch. It was hard to let go of, especially when all we got for it was $150.00. But I wouldn't think of it.

"We're on our way ... seems we should be singing, Rob. We're both singers. I moved Anja over the creases in the old truck and slid in beside her.

"Right," Rob called over his shoulder as he took off for one more check at the back door. His keys rattled in one hand while he held Natasha tight with the other.

"Wonder if the Israelites sang when they were pulling out of Egypt?" He gave me his quick smile that told me his mind was charged with the thought.

He reached over the diaper bag to hand Tasha to me, and I hugged her close. She needed only a receiving blanket over her diaper. It was a hot day for a little girl. Even though everything else was changing, nothing had changed about her. Her baby ways were the same. It seemed significant. Everything we did took on a significance. What it was ... I wasn't sure.

Anja leaned over me, and I could feel the dampness of her blonde hair as it was drying on her shoulders. I had watched the shampoo bubbles slide down the drain this morning, and I knew we were saying good-bye to a luxury.

From now on every drop of water we'd use would be carried from a spring. But we were geared for change. I welcomed it as part of this venture. Like pulling open the doors to God's seminary.

Rob looked over our place and with a nod, bowed his head at the front door. We would pray our good-bye to the beautiful home we had designed together. It seemed the house looked lonely. Like being left behind. More lonely than I felt. I could feel God's push. I was surprised when Rob mentioned the feeling ...

"You've heard me talking about the Israelites ever since we started this venture, Becky." Rob pulled my hand to his face as he looked at me.

"Do you really feel like one, Rob?"

"Yes, I do, Becky, but there is one difference. God was leading the Israelites. He seems to be pushing us."

We both felt it. We had to go.

We finished everything. We would take the keys back to the loan company. We were on our way.

I wondered, as we drove off, about the carrots, onions, and potatoes we had planted last spring. Let's see, they should be doing pretty good by now.

Will it always be like that up there, I mused as we pulled out of Spokane? When we find our way through those evergreens again, will we feel that stir of healing from the pine scent? Will it always feel like that? Healing for our hearts, our marriage? Up there - close to God ... I almost worried about my joy.

Our truck was speeding along pretty well for its

age as we turned off the Freeway to 395.

"Whew, glad that's over." Rob gave me his quick smile and patted my knee. "You know something, Becky, you're something else!"

ROB

The old truck drove along with no argument. A good buy. Now that we were on our way, I wanted that forest feel we knew on the mountain our first day up there. Becky had mentioned it. I had felt it, this now was absolute reality. And it wasn't without its pain.

"Sure was great of Dad to give us a chain saw, Rob," Becky said as she brushed the hair from Tasha's face. It was one more nudge of reality ... We needed that chain saw.

"Yeah. Sure was. Dad has a habit of patching up the leaks in the tire. Said if we were going to make it up there we'd need all the power we could get."

Driving along through the country was taking on a new twist. As I passed the farms, I wondered how others bought land. Planned their houses. Did they lay awake thinking of how they'd fell the trees or plow the soil? Most of all -- did they worry about the payments?

"Rob honey, stop! Stop!" I slammed on the brake. "What! What did we forget now?"

"Did you see that bathtub, Rob? That claw-foot bathtub?"

Someone else was having a yard sale. I wondered about the high hopes that went into this sale. Did someone struggle with the pain of parting with a claw-foot bathtub because they were going broke? ... or was it an eyesore they hoped to unload? Funny how thoughts like these hadn't plagued me before.

"Rob honey, how will we ever give the kids a bath without a tub? And we always wanted a claw-foot tub!"

I made a U-ie at the next farmer's drive. Becky was ecstatic. Hard to fathom that much jubilation over a tub! Anja was promised all the delights of water fun, and when Natasha got a little bigger, she'd play in it too. I priced the tub and bought it for twenty bucks. Left fifteen dollars in my wallet.

The farmer helped me push and shove. We had to make room for it. I shoved at the tool box until it just fit in a spot behind the tailgate.

Washington scenery! The towering evergreens always parted just enough to give you a vista of what they had hiding behind them. They parted enough to make the scenes that filled the card racks and pictures that were featured on calendars across the nation.

I wasn't numb to it. But I wasn't on vacation where I could let myself be transported with poetic thought. I knew that somewhere in that beauty there had to be a way to feed my family.

This time I checked the mileage. We had gone 55 miles when the sign said "Cheweleh". No turnoffs, just a town spread out on each side of the road.

The city bank, hardware store, and the Main Street grocery seemed to stand together, arm in arm, to greet us. Like they were chanting a well rehearsed welcome.

"We've been here long before you were cutting teeth, young man. Learn our ways, and we'll be your friend."

I wanted to become a part of this town. I wondered if the frontier men wavered between the enchantment of this land and a foreboding of what it was hiding.

I looked at Becky; she smiled back. As I often did, I wondered what she was thinking.

"Better get some groceries," I suggested.

"I've been thinking of that. Just the basics, Rob honey. I brought everything with us from our cupboards from home."

Becky went through the aisles like a pro picking out the essentials. As the clerk rang up our larder, I held my breath until she pressed total - Ten dollars? - Good! That left us five bucks for gas.

I carried out the bags. There were two of them, one on each arm. Becky followed in her familiar bend as she balanced a baby on one hip and held tight to a trusting uplifted little hand that knew Mama was leading her home.

I reached over the tailgate to give the tool box a shove.

"WHAT? COULDN'T BE! OUR TOOLS ARE GONE!"

"I LOVED HER LIKE NO OTHER ANIMAL"

ENTERPRISE: "UGLY TREE"

Chapter 6

BECKY

"Gone! No! No!" I cried, as my eyes riveted to the empty spot. I'd heard that your knees can turn to water. They do. This couldn't happen to us. Not us. In movies - yes. But not here when we are ready to start our climb to find God's answer.

No tools! The trees looked worse than giants. Whatever could Rob do with only his hands?

"Oh Rob," I cried. What magic words could I say? Our lives were depending on what Rob could do with those trees.

"We'd better get gas, honey, and we'd better get home."

Rob winced when I said 'home'. Inwardly, so did I. We didn't know what was awaiting us in that cabin up there sitting on stilts. But it was the only home we had now. He helped get the girls in the car and then slid in beside them.

I didn't ask him about the chain saw, but I had seen him slip it in behind the refrigerator. It must be there. Is this the way we begin? I looked at Rob and wondered what thoughts and fears he wasn't sharing with me.

Neither of us spoke. We just drove. Home? The word came with a jolt of nausea. What does that place look like? We hadn't even opened the door! We wanted only to flee what was destroying us so we grabbed at what the mountain offered.

Suddenly, the reality of what we left in Spokane when we handed the keys back to the mortgage company, converged with our reason for running. It prepared me. Whatever was in our little cabin up on that mountain, and what was crowded in the back of the truck was what we owned. *He will provide a way of escape.* It was like waiting for the next episode in learning His ways ...

"There's our turn, honey, better slow down," I said. Rob slowed down.

We were climbing our mountain, and once again the evergreens that bordered our drive created that same canyon-like feel that stirred my senses our first time up here. *'We are yours now, and we'll help you make it.'* I felt it, and it seemed like a voice from God.

ROB

We passed the spring; our mountain road wove up and up. I wondered if Becky felt as sick as I did. I felt stricken, almost helpless as I looked at the trees. But - not all was lost. Dad's chain saw, I remembered where I put it. Behind the refrigerator - that's where I put it. They didn't get everything.

Then the pungent perfume of pine hit me, and I surrendered some of my agony. Up here ... there had to be a way.

"You mean we own all this?" I asked God. Even

the hanging moss seemed a special part of some decor to greet us. We hadn't noticed it before. As my lungs filled with pine, I felt strength in my knees and power in my gut. Enough to drive directly to our cabin door.

Becky handed me the key. Somehow, I knew what was inside would not be good.

I opened the door and whew! The empty-place-smell was bad. The flies had made it in, and once in, could not make it out. They reminded me that they had tried for they were piled in heaps around the floor and in all corners. The windows were splattered with their efforts as they crashed against them.

There was a scurry of darting little animals squeaking their objections to us.

How does a man bring his wife and babies into this? I leaned against the door jam and questioned my sanity. I saw myself through others' eyes. Finally. Their questions about what we were about to do had been ignored by our determination.

"Do you guys really know what you're doing?" Randy asked it. The folks asked it. Not in so many words but with a quick turn of a shoulder, or a walk out of the room when there was no more to be said.

It wasn't -- could I cope with this? Men can cope with water filled trenches for days. But Becky? With her long fingernails and shoulder length curls? The little girls? How can little Anja walk into her new home crunching dead flies with every step?

"What can I say? Becky, it's worse in there than you can imagine."

"What do you mean worse, Rob? I've been imagining just how terrible it can be. I saw that movie where the door fell off the oven and they found a raccoon in it! We have to go in unless you want to sleep in the truck."

Preparing her wouldn't help. Besides, she had handed me the baby and was taking the steps to the door. I hunched my shoulders and waited. Waited as people wait when they expect an explosion. It came.

"Yikes!"

"It's terrible, Becky, I know."

"Boy, where do we start? Have to clear out the flies, Rob. First bring in the broom and the dust pan.

"Here, give me the baby, Rob. That claw-foot bathtub, honey, we can put the kids in that." I marveled at the can-do spirit of my wife, as she helped me get that hippo of a bathtub up the steps and through the door.

She draped it with blankets, took off their shoes, and the youngsters had a clean spot, where they could watch something I hoped they wouldn't remember.

It was a quick plan, but I knew it would work. Becky lived by it. Start in one corner and work your way around.

I emptied a huge garbage bag of shoes into the truck bed and brought it in. The bag was more important than shoes now. As I swept, Becky held the dust pan.

"Take a swipe at the logs and any shelf as you make the rounds, Rob."

Bag after bag of dead flies were dumped on the edge of the clearing. We should have counted them. We were making headway faster than I could imagine. Along with the flies went cobwebs and pieces of straw our former tenants had left behind as they scurried along the logs.

"The stove will have to go under that chimney, Rob, so we'll have to put our table under this window." The zest in her voice was bracing and good as she designed her nest.

But when I stepped outside and looked over the expanse of what I could see of our forest, I envied her. Her destiny was to nurture life and was bracketed by those log walls. It was more predictable, I felt.

I uncovered my ax and hammer under the seat of the pick up and began my course in total wholehearted gratitude. "They didn't get everything," I shouted.

The intoxication of the pine and the walled in closeness of the mountains kept me vacillating between a heady joy because of the spot we had found, and the stark reality of making a living off this land.

I had no plan. I wondered if one would come. Starting in one corner and working your way around wouldn't do it for me.

Chapter 7

BECKY

"Rob!" I gave him a nudge that bolted him upright. "Do you see what I see?" I slid under the covers.

"Can't believe it!" Rob shook himself and stared back. "How many are there?"

We were all snuggled together on the floor in our sleeping bags, in an aroma of scrubbed freshness we had thought impossible a few hours ago. Amazing what a few drops of pine-sol and a few buckets of water can do to a room that had reeked of old dust and dead things.

Circled overhead on the rim of our A Frame balcony, were eyes. Three little heads with glowing little eyes beamed their disgust with us from a hole in the corner as though sizing up the invaders of their paradise. They scampered and squealed their horror of us.

"Guess they come with the territory," Rob said and punched his pillow to bury his head.

"What's that?" I screamed, "Oh Rob!" A flurry and fluster of something as big as a cat collided with the cans I had pushed in the corner by the stove.

"Oh Rob!" I grabbed for my bundles of babies we

had next to us.

"Most likely the granddaughter of that raccoon those city slickers chased out of their oven."

"Honey, will it always be like this?" I knew there were holes in the corners that wouldn't shut out anything smaller than a cat that might want to visit us. The scrub water kept running down there when we rinsed the floor last night.

"Not after I plug up the leaks in this place, Becky. Can't we try and get some sleep so I won't have the blind-staggers tomorrow? I have to do battle with the elements out there, and I need some shut eye."

That's what I needed too. Some shut eye. Camping was never quite like this. Maybe because we had never invaded a spot that was so completely the territory of mice, rats and raccoons before. I was awake now and sleep was far from me.

I didn't feel abandoned by God up here. I knew I had no right to claim instant rewards on this mountain. We had come here to learn God's ways, and hadn't I wanted my hurrahs from the world too?

Oh Lord, I wanted to model almost as much as I wanted to be a singer, and I know that becoming a mother saved me from becoming ensnared by the entertainment world. Rob was out there trying to make a living while exposed to every kind temptation. It was easier for me.

Rob thinks I don't understand him ... but I do. He got hooked on alcohol, but I'm still hooked on cigarettes. Two packs a day and I can't shake the habit. They don't dilute my judgment, but they corrode my lungs. We must overcome. If it takes rats and raccoons, Lord, we must overcome. This mountain is for me, too. Finally, I fell asleep.

Food - it became our total concern. With me - it

was an obsession. Rob was building a shed for his tools; the few he salvaged when we unloaded the truck. He had dragged up some lumber he found around an old barn below us. A place for his tools had become his obsession. He must lock them up. We may starve while he's doing it, but he says he cannot tackle the trees with his fists. He must put them under lock and key.

But what about the children?

Though we may encounter the rigors of soul discipline, our kids must not suffer. I knew the thought was haunting Rob too, but not for long. Randy answered our greatest concern. His brother arrived with cases and cases of Similac in the trunk of his car.

"The suppliers keep our cupboards stocked with new products. Wonders like this, and I knew two little cuties who might use them right now," he said.

"They won't miss a vitamin on this stuff." He looked around with an air of amused appraisal. "You're doing alright, Kid." He gave his brother the accustomed slap on the back.

"Now, if you get short of something, you will buzz my line, OK?" He turned the key on his car and we heard the roar of his strong engine taking him back to a civilization we wanted no part of. We felt he understood that.

But I knew Rob's pride would never admit that we weren't eating too good.

The garden became our total nourishment. I thought of Scarlett digging through the weeds of Tara for a carrot as I salvaged our meals.

"Try these!" Rob waved some pigweed above his head as though he had discovered a lode in the hills. "I read about this stuff. Full of vitamins."

It was. Mild tasting and mixed with our onions,

carrots and potatoes, which were about the size of small eggs, it was good. It was food. Real nourishing food.

We prayed before we ate, and we prayed as we ate. We began to know hunger pangs. Yet, I knew Rob's pride wouldn't let him ask anybody for help. Especially now that the children were looking rosy and pink with health.

We couldn't admit to anybody that we were not able to hack it. Nobody thought we could make it up here. Were we going to prove them right?

"Becky! Becky!" Rob came running from the shed swinging some garish looking metal things.

"I found these traps!" He turned them over and tested their snap. "Remember when we bought them in Missoula at that yard sale and you wondered what we'd ever do with something like this? Well, we're going to find out!"

"Why did you ever bring them with you, Rob? What are you going to do with them?" I backed off from something with that ghoulish design.

"We'll trap some squirrels, Becky. Meat! Can you remember how it tastes? When these things didn't sell at the yard sale, I couldn't toss them, and now they're going to get us some meat. Can you remember how it tastes?"

"Oh Rob, I'll make stew. I have flour, enough for some biscuits. Oh, Rob honey, I'll make stew."

I watched the traps. We had baited them with the last of the peanut butter. I watched the squirrels hopping around and over them but never in them. And never had I seen so many squirrels. They hopped from branch to branch, except the branch where we had our traps.

I couldn't concentrate on anything else. They drew me. Every fifteen minutes I'd make the rounds checking the traps. I was so hungry. No matter what I was doing,

I'd detour around the traps, checking them.

I would skin them myself, and cut them up. I was hungry enough to do that! I would have the stew ready when Rob came in from the woods. All I could think of was stew. The carrots were gone. The onions, the potatoes were gone. So was the pigweed. But I had flour to thicken the stew. I could smell it. Taste it.

The chain saw was a constant reminder of a hungry man out there. Rob was cutting firewood to sell it. We had to get money. We had learned that lesson at the grocery store. The forest was our only resource.

The calendar days were X'd since the last day we had eaten anything at all. Four days - my stomach felt sick and actually, maybe I felt less hungry than sick. We were drinking lots of water, even drinking it hot, and still it made me sick. *Lord, help Rob. How can he keep on out there in this draining heat, sawing and piling, sawing and piling those logs that he's going to sell?*

The thought entered my mind. Maybe he should have some Similac so he would have strength to do this. But when I mentioned it to Rob, he said it sounded like genocide. Actually taking food from the children!

But he had to keep going! I had to do what I had to do. I opened a can of Similac and stirred in my last bit of flour. Every pinch meant nourishment. So every pinch was salvaged from the bottom of the can; whatever rolled out on the counter, it was used. I rolled it out and baked it, hard and crisp. We finished it off with the last jar of jam I had made from the service berries I found when we first came up here. Perhaps nothing will equal that delicacy.

I still had a piece of Irish Spring soap, so I washed the diapers and clothes and hung them over the bushes. It was a thing mothers do, and it felt like a tie to something normal. But mothers also eat.

Fifth day -- no squirrels! Sixth day! Nothing! God was not supplying manna for these followers!

"Oh Jesus," I cried, as I watched Rob tripping over the underbrush and swatting at mosquitos. He seemed to be searching for a branch or tree that he could get the saw to cut through. I had followed the buzz of his saw.

"That saw, Lord, it's gotten so dull and all his filing doesn't seem to sharpen it. Oh Jesus, help his faith. I worry about him, He doesn't look right. Oh God, I worry about him." I sobbed and wiped the sweat, tears, and briars from my face with the towel I carried to swish away the cloud of mosquitos that circled my head.

"Lord, he's not acting right. Is it alcohol withdrawal? Is it hunger? Oh God. Oh God. Oh God." I ran to the house to check on the girls.

I collapsed into our blue chair and shook with sobs. "If he gets too discouraged, Lord, he won't do anything to himself again, will he?

"What is he thinking, Lord? Oh God, he's not thinking about Rita is he? He's not thinking of giving up and going back to her? Why won't he look at me? He just heads for the door with his water jug and stays out there all day. Oh God, I didn't think it would be like this!"

I heard his step on the porch and jumped up to meet him. I wanted him near even if his mind might be far away.

ROB

"Becky, I have to go down the hill to a phone and

call Mom. We haven't called her since we came up here."

"Rob, whatever do you mean, call Mom? Something's not right Rob." Becky grabbed my shoulders and shook me. "I can tell when something's not right with you. You haven't looked me in the eye for two days. "Her hair was flying, her face red from crying. "You have no intention of calling your mother and you know it!"

She convulsed with sobs as she shook me. "You - want - to - call - Rita, - Rob. You - know - that's - what - you - intend - to - do," she screamed.

She was right. That was my intention. For days I couldn't let go of the thought that Rita was wondering about me. Crying when she heard what happened to me. I couldn't even pray anymore. The thought that I should call her became very right to me. Was it all that wrong to let her know I was OK?

Becky thought so. "Rob, don't you know how much I love you? I came up on this mountain because I loved you. I came up here to save our marriage. I know you are suffering from withdrawal. I know what withdrawal is. I can understand that. I'm hooked on cigarettes. But Rita, I can't understand. You have to cut your ties with Rita!" She was hurt and she was angry.

"I can't take it Rob. I can't." She clung to me as she sobbed on my shoulder. "Do you really want to just give up? Is that what you want to do?"

It seemed my conscience suddenly shifted into its rightful course. My wife! My Becky! I'm killing her because I've crushed her heart - "O God."

I fell to my knees and brought her with me. "Oh Becky," I sobbed. "Forgive me if you can. I'm not worthy of your love. I'm not worthy to be loved by someone like you, and I can't imagine why you stick with me."

"Because I love you, Rob. Oh Rob, I can't let go of you. Won't you stick it out here and see what God can do with us?"

We clung to each other as we cried together and felt closer than we had for months. She forgave me. Again and again, she told me that she forgave me.

We found that in our hunger, our souls grew closer to God than we had ever known, even though our cries seemed to go unheard. "A humble and a contrite heart ..." I read from the scripture that night.

"Just a minute, Rob," Becky said. "Let's look up 'contrite' in Webster's. See what it means. "'To bruise, rub, grind to powder,'" she read.

"We cried our prayer together. "Do Your work, Lord, Do Your work."

The water diet held for another day as the squirrels hopped over our traps - held until I finally had a cord of wood on the truck and was ready for take off.

"Honey, there's hardly any gas in the truck."

"I'll pray my way to town," I said.

Pray? After seven days with no squirrels in my traps, but I didn't speak those thoughts to Becky.

I put my Bible on the seat beside me. "I'll bring home food Becky," I promised.

Hungry and hot! This discipline of God was no circus act! I wiped at the sweat pouring down my neck with an overused bandanna. Our mountain had surely become my proving ground.

The truck started. Great! I can coast down to Chewelah. Once I'm there, I should have enough gas to find a spot to park it.

The truck coasted along, but when it slowed to a crawl as the hill leveled out, it stopped. I had to restart the motor. Each whip of the accelerator I could feel in my gut. Was the gas gone? Each curve was an encounter and a trophy when I inched around it.

The Safeway Store! I made it! Good place! I thanked the Lord. People who stock up on grub must think of winter days when they need wood! I found my spot and crawled out to post my sign.

Firewood $40.00.

Whew, was it hot in the sun! But inside the truck it felt like a furnace. The car cushions felt blistered. I picked up the water jug, and what I downed tasted like yesterday's stale tea. But no matter, we'd soon have food.

I tried to think of what I'd bring home. We needed everything. Becky should have given me a list, but where would she start? Where would she stop?

People were finding their cars in the Safeway parking lot with their carts loaded. Some were pushing two carts. They'd pile the bags in the trunk and then they'd fill up the back seat. Funny how matter of fact they were about it all. Had they ever tried going without food for seven days?

"What's the matter with these people? ... they don't even notice I'm here. Can't they hear my stomach growling? Would they stop if they could?"

I picked up my Bible and found Romans. It has a chapter about tribulation. About faith. About forgiveness. *Blessed is the man whose iniquities are forgiven, and whose sins are covered.* I leaned back to pray my worship. Can I believe that? *Me ... forgiven? My sins ... covered?*

Oh Lord, ... I beg Your forgiveness. Cover me as You promised.

Forgiven! I was transported into the reality of it. *O what glory fills my soul,* wrote the songwriter. I sang it and the words washed over me as I sat in the heat of my truck.

I have been vain - wanted to sing - wanted to hear the applause. I was ready to sell my soul for it. *But You spared me, Lord. The belt broke.*

Don't people know that when someone is trying to sell wood on a blistering day like this in August he must be desperate? Would they care if they knew? They drove around me and my sign without so much as a glance my way.

I slashed the $40,00 to $35.00. That should tell people something! Anyone cutting the price on a load of this wood must need to sell it. Bad!

A bunch of people poured out of the Park Side Inn, laughing, lighting up, overfed.

Lord when I leave an eat-shop again, I'll wonder who might be watching, who hasn't eaten for seven days.

I read on - *Therefore being justified by faith, we have peace with God through our Lord Jesus Christ.*

But Lord, I have to sell this wood. I have babies. I have Becky. What I'm doing is not wrong. It's hard to have peace when I'm so hungry. Help me sell this wood.

$30.00 - I slashed it again.

Tribulation worketh patience, we glory in tribulation!

Either they don't turn their head or they look and then drive on! This is good wood! It's getting dusky. Sun's going down. Must be past eight o'clock. What is Becky doing with the children? Has she promised them great things when Daddy comes home? I can't even get home to her. I have no gas. And I can't phone. We have no phone!

I glanced at my image in the mirror. Man, I'm a

mess! Heat must have hatched a whole batch of new whiskers. Hair kinked around my shoulders. Trousers bunched around my middle. I should have tightened my belt - punched a new hole.

Brother, I am thin. I am gaunt, and I have to sell this wood.

I noticed the phone booth. Should I call the folks? Haven't even had gas to run down the hill and find a phone. I wonder what Mom would think if I call collect?

"Rob." I heard her anxiety. "Are you sure you're alright?"

"We're making it Mom."

"Your voice sounds so weary. What are you doing for money?"

"We'll be OK. I have a load of wood to sell."

"Are you eating alright? How about Becky and the kids?"

"Well, it's been pretty slim picking, but we should be making it now!"

"You don't sound alright to me."

"I got to get back to the truck, Mom. Folks seem to be stocking up at Safeway today. They'll be buying my wood on the way home."

"Rob, if you're having trouble, why don't you say so. Others take help. That doesn't mean you're a loser. We all get stuck on a slippery hill sometimes and no matter how we gun the motor we only slip and slide. All it takes is a shove. A shove so we can make the hill, and once we make it, we're ready to help the next guy. Think about it Rob. Can't we help?"

"We have thought about it, Mom. With us it's different. We're not out here because fate dumped us here. It's not like losing a job and being down and out. We can't ask for help. We chose this mountain for the lessons God can teach us here. We have to make it. I have this wood to sell. We'll do OK. The kids are fine. Randy brought them enough food to last them half a year."

I heard a sob as she hung up. I didn't think she could understand. She still worries about us, and food and shelter are her concerns.

They are ours too - but also - there are lessons. God's lessons.

I hung up and went back to the truck and marked the price down to $25.00.

$25.00! How can anybody pass up a bargain like this? This is good wood! Even if the day is a scorcher.

But they did. In droves. I felt beaten. Moments came when I was so sick I wanted to abandon ship. Leave the rig and head for home. See how Becky was faring. But I couldn't. To turn back now would have been a violation of everything that the day had imprinted on my soul. Everything I had just told Mom. We can't give up!

"I'll stay, Lord. I'll stand by this truck."

I dozed. I cried. I prayed. I begged God. My total prayer was - "Help me sell this wood!"

A car slowed but I didn't look up. I couldn't take the pain when it drove on. But this car stopped!

"How much wood you got there?" asked a man, sandy colored from hair to shoe. He had one singular quality. He asked about my wood.

"A cord!"

"Take twenty bucks for it?"

"Twenty bucks! Man, I worked a whole week to cut this wood. It's dry." I had to bargain. It was our living. "Right size for a quick fire. Doesn't have to be split."

"Ok - I know that. But you should be out here selling ice, not firewood, my friend! Twenty bucks, it's all I got." He dangled the twenty dollar bill from his empty wallet.

Money! Twenty dollars of it. "OK. it's a deal!"

He noticed my Bible on the dashboard. "You a Jesus Freak or something?"

"I don't know. I'm not a freak! I'm serving Jesus." It was my first testimony.

"Shake hands," he said, "I'm a Christian too. Follow me to my house and we'll unload this." He drove off with me praying that the truck would start and get me to the home of this man with that twenty dollar bill. It did.

"That looks like good dry wood, young man. I'll be needing about 8-10 cords come fall. How about forty dollars a cord?"

Money! I had found a way to make it. I had learned we could not make it on that mountain without it. I ran the twenty back and forth in my hand. Money! I'll put some gas in the tank and head for the supermarket.

"Becky, I'm on my way home!" With gas in the tank and the staples of life bouncing in the seat beside me, the road home seemed short. Oranges I had, and apples too. How is Becky holding up?

I was soon to find out.

BECKY

Anja threw kisses and I waved Tasha's hand until Rob's truck turned the bend. We could hear the roar of his truck dim and disappear and get replaced by the sweet-toned hymns from the trees overhead.

Oh, this place, how I love it. Would there ever be a time when people could live without money? Out here we seem more aligned to people who walked the earth without such a reliance on money. But we can't claim this land unless we pay for it.

I hugged Tasha. Scientific advances haven't changed our babies. They still snuggle as warm and close as ever. *But, oh dear God, they still must eat! Help Rob sell his wood.*

I climbed the porch steps. They needed a nail here and there to steady them. Rob will have to get at it. Already the house was sweltering and the water heating on the stove made it muggy. The piles of clothes never looked bigger.

Oh, maybe we could pick up a washer at a yard sale. I wondered if anyone else was still rubbing clothes out by hand. I wouldn't want to be the only one left out in the industrial revolution.

Seems I have been left out ... an awful lot. When I am hurting, I think of my mother. My beautiful, wonderful mother.

I fixed Tasha's bottle and propped her in her crib. She took it as though nothing in the world was wrong. But Anja - should I promise her the goodies that Daddy would be bringing home from town? She wanted me to read from her Three Bear book. She wanted me to play ball. She ran up with her wagon and wanted me to run down the hill with her.

"Anja, Mommy has to wash all these clothes and try and get the place nice and clean before Daddy gets home."

"Now, Mommy. Now, read my book."

I looked at the six piles of clothes on the floor. The house was almost black with flies.

"I'll have to chase out these flies, honeygirl. Maybe you could help Mommy chase these flies."

But now, Mommy, read my book now."

"Oh, honey, can't you give your ball a ride in your wagon? After a while Mommy will lay down with you and then I'll read your book." I knew if I sat down now I could never get up. I was so weak and I was so hungry.

She ran out to try my idea. She stumbled over the root that popped through our uneven ground and bruised her knee. She cried, and I had used our last band-aide yesterday.

"Daddy will fix our yard, honey." I blew on it.

"It still hurts, Mommy." My remedy was a wet cloth, and it seemed to work. She rolled over in her blanket and fell asleep. I was ashamed to feel relieved that it took a bruised knee, but now I could get at the wash.

"Oh, it's hot!" Thank God we had electricity. I turned on the fan and scrubbed the dirt spots with the sliver of soap I had left. Hope Rob remembers soap.

I felt sick. How ever would I make it? I'd have to work fast. I learned I could pump up my energy by mentally shifting into high gear. Amazing what an energizer "have to" can be. Was that what powered the clearing of this land for these country farms before they had power saws?

The thought that I had been really left out would not buzz off. I had lost my mother. Won't I ever get over it?

God, I am grateful for the new mother You gave us. She was wonderful. Six of us. How did she do it? But I thought of my own mother. I looked like her. She must have had dreams for me, and I never got to hear them.

Funny how the thoughts of Rita kept coming back by the boat full. How could Rob fall in love with her? She wasn't pretty. She couldn't sing. If I thought of her ... how about him? How often has he thought of her? In his heart of hearts, is he still wishing he could marry her, because life would be easier with her?

I can't get these thoughts out of my mind, Lord. Is this my addiction? Feeling sorry for myself? I scrubbed the diapers and threw them in the boiler. It felt good to hear them splash as they hit the hot water. My sliver of Irish Spring was getting thinner, and I had to stretch it, but it's hard to go easy when you're as mad as I am.

I thought I'd forgiven him. *Oh God, what kind of forgiveness is this? Don't you see God? Not only did she steal my husband, but she filled my heart with hate. And I can't get rid of the hate - so I lose both ways. Are happy wives better Christians than I am? When I feel like this I can't sing my song -- I can't think of Your Word. I only sin. With my thinking, I sin.*

The piles of clothes went through the rubbing, the boiling and rinsing. I stretched them over the bushes.

"When will I get a clothesline?" I learned to snap one end of a diaper until it whipped over the branch.

"And the holes in the house! They aren't fixed yet either. Oh I know he had to cut the wood. He's weak, and he's been working all the time, but that doesn't plug the holes in the ceiling. And it doesn't plug the holes in the floor. And now I'm even talking to myself again.

"Will we ever get this place fixed before winter? Will we ever eat? I wonder how he's faring with selling that wood?"

I had finished the wash and mopped the floor clean with the rinse water. I remembered my song and sang it as loud as I had voice.

I shouted it! *I surrender all -- do you hear that, Lord? ... I surrender all. All to Jesus I surrender. I surrender all!*

My spirit sweetened and I noticed what the sweet aroma of a fresh washed wood floor can do to assist the struggle to be happy. The thought that my sister had married well and didn't have to run to a mountain to save her marriage flit through my mind, but I had felt the touch of The Spirit on my soul. The comparison to my sister didn't stick this time.

Help me, Lord, to keep singing my song.

It was getting dark ... "Suppose Rob doesn't sell that wood at all? What then?" But I sang and sang and sang. *I surrender all.*

"Anja. honey, wake up. Let's go down to Big Rock and wait for Daddy. It's nice and cool down there."

I carried Tasha, and Anja ran ahead to climb up on the boulder that was ours because we claimed this land. We called it simply Big Rock. It sat as a testament, marking the spot of ground where we would learn the ways of God.

Anja brought her book, and I had no trouble reading it in the shadows. She'd correct my mistakes. She knew the pages by heart. Tasha chewed on her bottle. We looked and looked down the road for a light.

I would not allow myself thought. When I wasn't reading, I was singing. We kept waiting. At times I wondered what he was doing. Would he remember soap? Would he bring an apple? Oh, how I wanted a dish of ice cream. I was sure he wouldn't indulge in such a luxury. Would I ever be in a spot where I could eat ice cream again and not think of Big Rock?

"Don't get off the rock, honey. You might step on a thistle." I wonder if Rob will remember that we didn't have band-aides?

"Sing, Anja, sing with Mommy."

"Climb up Sunshine Mountain," she began. The old Sunday School song I used to sing when I thought that all of God's mountains were Sunshine Mountains. Someday I'll have to tell her that God has mountains that help us learn His ways.

We tossed the ball, sang every song we knew, and then sang them over. The sun dropped, and we sat there still. Mosquitos found us.

Anja found little twigs so we could chase them. Finally her head nodded and fell on my breast next to Tasha. I couldn't forsake this vigil. I had to wait. What has happened to Rob? *Dear Lord, Whatever has happened to Rob?*

Finally a glimmer crossed the road. It became brighter until I heard the familiar rumble of our old motor.

"Anja, Anja, wake up." I shook her awake. "Do you see the light, honeygirl?"

"Is that Daddy?"

"Has to be. Listen to the roar and rattle -- has to be his truck." It was.

"Becky, I got food! Food!" He hugged us until it hurt. He danced with Tasha and then had to dance with Anja. He hugged me. "Let's go home and eat!"

Hot dogs -- a feast for a king. And ice cream. I let it slip down my throat like a tonic. Cool, sweet, strawberry ice cream. We feasted and were giddy with the moment. We knew we would never forget. The first taste of food after seven days!

To feel strong again. To laugh again. Rob laughed when he told how he was unnoticed, ignored, possibly scorned. Did a crazy jig to see if his pants would really fall off. Threatened to shave. I agreed with that.

"Is that a light coming through the woods? It filtered through the trees and then gave a sudden lightning flash as the car climbed upward.

"It is a car, Rob. Did you break a law, or something?"

"Not that I know of." He wiped the lather off his face.

"Honey, isn't that the folks?" We ran outside.

"Say, what gives anyway? This isn't the time you folks usually pick to visit." We were at the car doors pulling them out from each side.

"Rob, when you called today, I felt it was time for a visit regardless of what the hour was. Tell me Son, did you sell that wood?"

"He did! He did!" I cried. "He sold the wood and got orders for eight to ten more cords come fall, for forty dollars a cord." I was shouting.

"Well, that calls for a celebration!" Dad said as he started unloading the car. The trunk, the back seat, there was food everywhere. We noticed a limp as he tried carrying in the packages.

"What's the matter, Dad? What happened?" Rob asked as he relieved him of his packages. Dad grabbed the side rail as he climbed the stairs.

"A little back trouble since the accident. That's one reason why we're here."

"Yes, Rob," Mom interjected. "He's having so much trouble driving. We were wondering if you could drive for a few weeks so he can make his route. He could prop himself in the back seat and give that back a rest.

There was an aroma permeating our cabin that didn't come from grocery bags. Even though we had finished off the hot dogs, we were ready to start over. When Mom uncovered her casserole it drew us like a magnet.

Putting our feet under the table together took on new meaning. Thanking God for food took on new meaning. It would never become a perfunctory ritual in our house. Our mountain had taught us.

"This was pretty great of you guys," Rob told his mother. "That casserole, I think I ate half of it."

"Rob, when I heard your voice I was overjoyed. I told Dad we should finish this meal with the kids."

"How can I ever thank you guys?" Rob asked.

Food, food, food, and now a way to make some money before its wood-selling time in the fall. What a day! I praised God. We all prayed and praised God. And I prayed for those who were still waiting to find a way. I always would. I always would!

ROB

Mom! She walks so straight and with her silvered hair flipped around her head, she looks great. I've always been proud of her ... was there anything wrong in wanting to return the favor? Make her proud of me?

I certainly wasn't one of her shining stars. Younger than Randy (her doctor son), I often wondered how she explained me to her friends. I've always wanted to make her a great gardener that grew fine sons. When I was singing, I thought that day was right around the corner. Now ... God knows. I said it reverently.

"Anything wrong?" Becky asked while we were watching their car roll down our driveway. She felt my quietness and noticed my involvement with the yard sale can opener while the folks were here. She felt it meant something.

"When something's wrong you don't talk, you fidget. Many times she had told me that. She had talked. Her chatter had been nonstop as she and Mom decided how much the girls had grown. Mom would be able to describe the Big Rock experience where they had waited for me to come home.

Becky was at her jubilant best when they were here. She radiated. God had come through with her needs, and she let the folks know they were a part of it. She had soap, shampoo, band-aides. She was set for tomorrow.

I noticed her eye shadow and the help she had

given to her glowing cheeks. Man, is she beautiful!

"Wrong, Becky? Nothing, just had a roller-coaster day."

"I know. It must have been terrible, waiting for that one sale. But honey, look! Look, how the Lord blessed us today!" She crawled into my lap and tousled my hair. "I'll wash this stuff tomorrow," she said as she hugged my face to her.

Everyone sleeps better than I do these days ... I could hear Becky's light lovely breathing sounds as she cuddled next to me on the floor. The girls were sleeping in their crib, and I was staring at the rafters. The full moon was taunting me ... I hadn't gotten to the holes yet and the moon shone through. And I could hear something stirring beneath us. Same raccoons ... I hadn't fixed those holes either. I had only cut wood.

Twenty lousy dollars worth of wood!

Funny, what a teeter-totter day this had turned out to be. The harder my end of the plank hits bottom, the higher Becky rises on the other end. She's supportive and good. Trusting and grateful.

I tried to feast my thoughts on the lessons I had learned today. What came to my mind was a thought I think I heard somewhere. "God's grace is free -- but at the grocery store, I pay cash." Like for band-aides, shampoo and soap. Forgive me for thinking that, Lord.

Might as well go sit on the steps. The sky wasn't full of stars. Couldn't see that much of the sky tonight, and I liked that. I didn't feel like scanning a universe tonight. The few stars allowed to peek through our hole in the trees seemed meant for just me. I thought of Henry David Thoreau, "Who can own the sky?" This bit above me seemed mine alone. Who else could see it?

The mourning doves were rolling out a sort of purring sound to each other. You could hear their breathing punctuate their soft monotone until their contentment seemed so intense you knew they wanted to live on forever. Here. So do I ... if I can only make a living here. I could cut wood. We could get a cow, a jersey cow, with milk so rich it tastes like cream. Chickens, a garden. I could suddenly feel the strength that tells a forest ... move over a bit ... we have dominion here ... God says so.

Strength to build a shed. To fix the cabin, to cut wood, to get a cow ...

Strength to deaden the thoughts that disturb. The fluttering thoughts of Rita and her easy laughter. Where I didn't have to climb, to stretch, to reach. Where I was "good enough" as I was. "If it makes you happy -- do it!"

Where my performance scale was never measured. "Relax kid, don't let it bother you."

I haven't scored very high so far, Lord. The unbothered way, Lord, help me to shake its pull.

What makes the Christian strive on? Like Christian in Pilgrim's Progress - fleeing from the wrath to come? And like Christ - who for the joy that was set before Him - endured?

Restore the joy of my salvation. I need the joy of it, now Lord. "Moment by Moment." Like the song writer, I knew I would pray this prayer again. Constantly.

I crawled in and tried to sleep. Man, what I wouldn't give for the assist of a little wine. Funny, when I was starving and struggling with that impossible saw, I didn't miss it much. The struggle to get something for my family to eat overpowered the pull of alcohol. I'd fall asleep before I hit the pillow.

Is this the way it's going to be, Lord? "He will be my

peace." Oh Lord, I claim it. Thank you for the barrier between me and the bottle. Feast my mind on Thee, Lord. Help me through this withdrawal.

I woke up wondering where to start. There was no 'corner' for me that Becky talks about. I would tackle that mass of tangled trees and when I got winded, I would fix the porch. A schedule like that might do it. I'll call Dad in the afternoon and find out about the driving job.

"Breakfast's ready, Rob. Eggs! Toast! Coffee!"

"Man, I am starved." I grabbed her and held her hard as I promised, "We'll have food on this table, Becky, I promise you, food on this table."

BECKY

"Do you hear what I hear?" I heard a car in our drive and ran to the door. "We haven't had any visitors up here except your folks last night, Rob." When I single-handed the bedrolls to the corner, we had an instant parlor.

Rob gulped a swallow of coffee and peered over my shoulder through the window. "Well, I'll be. I envy that guy for his silver 4 wheel pick up."

It stopped right beside our steps that needed the nails. My teeth felt edgy as he reached them in a couple of strides.

A man, appearing completely occupied with his mission, mounted our jiggly steps with no trouble.

"Should I open the door, Becky?" Rob whispered.

"Of course, Silly. We haven't lost all our manners,"

He wore a neat suit and had a face that would make you think him kind, but I would never know what lines or expressions told me that. Rob opened the door.

"Good morning," he said, and extended his hand. "I'm Don Bowe from the Addy New Life Christian Center.

I wanted to welcome you to our part of Washington."

Whatever got into Rob I wasn't sure. I think he tried to sound laid back, even a bit urbane. "Well, I hope you didn't come for a donation. Because money, we don't have much of that!" He laughed, and I felt he wished he hadn't said that, because this humble person looked around with an air of admiration and understanding."

"Next time. "No donations today." He put us instantly at ease. "Actually, your mother phoned yesterday and asked me to call."

"Then you know pretty much about us." I led him to our one blue lounge chair.

"Well, actually, she said you had been having some problems and thought a chance to talk them over with a fellow Christian might help."

I had wanted to go for counseling, but Rob had wanted to work it out on this mountain. He had said it would be would be easier for him to take his whipping from our mountain. And it was my suggestion to come up here ... so I'd stick to it and let the mountain do its work.

But I admitted, "I've always felt it might help to talk to someone."

"It does," Don assured us. "Maybe not talk it out. Yell it out! Scream it out! Holler it out! We are all fellow pilgrims. Remember this - 'There is no temptation taken you but such as is common to man.'"

Common to man! Funny I hadn't thought of that. Of course it's in the Bible. "He will, with the temptation, provide a way of escape so you may be able to bear it." We will be able to bear it! We would be able to overcome! When the plaguing thoughts return ... they are common to man. We would be able to bear it.

Rob must have shared my thoughts. "You know,

you have helped me already," he said. "You really have." I knew he wasn't ready to bare his soul to anyone but God, and I wouldn't push him.

He had coffee with us as we finished our breakfast. He told us about his work at the Christian Center, and Rob and I told him we were going to overcome on our mountain. He had radiated the love of Jesus as we were to start another day of accepting the ways of God.

"Anything worthwhile is going to take hard work," said this loving Christian who didn't try to varnish our undertaking with promises or platitudes.

"We're ready for that!" Our spirits had risen with his visit.

"I hope you're ready to see a lot of us," Rob said as he left.

ROB

On Thee, the Solid Rock, I stand ... all other ground ... is sinking sand. I woke up to the words I had sung since a kid. Rhyming words that had imprinted a truth. Despite our problems up here, the ground felt solid on this path. I knew the difference. I had just come from sinking sand.

Becky tucked the covers around the girls. The mornings were cool even when we had sweltered through yesterday's heat. She was deciding what to make for breakfast. A milestone. Deciding what to eat! It was up to me to keep that one of her problems. I stepped outside to size up the weather, and I heard the birds stirring for a new day. Becky had mentioned that the birds' morning song had become her wake-up call. She observed how they matched their patterns to their instinctive drives. Makes us wonder how we fit into God's great plan of it all.

Cut wood? Fix the steps? Too early to call Dad about the driving job. I walked along the paths that we had been making up here. We were changing the earth. Even the spot where I had taken the firewood had changed it -- it extended our space. You can't do that when your space has been cemented around you by city planners. Oh, but it's good up here. I drew in the morning freshness and remembered again that God gave man dominion over His creation. The responsibility would always be a part of my worship.

"Breakfast's ready!" There was a new significance to her call. The smell of toast, coffee, and bacon! Frying bacon! Always reminds me of Nanny and the gentleness she added to her world. Has to be the world's best smell. I remembered yesterday's ache of breathing the food smells of what someone else was eating and wondering when I'd eat again.

Becky was at her best at snapping me into the here and now. "Honey, do you suppose we should make plans for church tomorrow? You more or less promised we'd come."

"Guess I did, didn't I? What all will it involve?"

Anja and I sat across from Becky and the baby. I noted how much Anja resembled her mother.

"Say grace, Rob."

As we reached for each other's hands, there was nothing I could say that would tell the Lord what I felt. My heart must tell Him. 'God looketh on the heart' - I knew He could see mine, could find the explosion of reverence for His ways.

"We really don't have church clothes anymore, Rob.

I can't believe it has been that long since we attended church. But I'll find something."

"Find something for me too. Better not try out my leather pants on them."

"Fun--ny!"

"No, I mean it." Suddenly I was aware of a responsibility to these people. We shouldn't offend their ways. "Don't really know what I got that would be proper for church. The crowd up here is going to be quite conservative. I could tell that from watching the shoppers yesterday. Not a hip dresser in the bunch."

We tried. Becky made a quite a heap of the duds she had tried on and didn't think would make it at the community church. Too tight! Too short! But the earrings? She wasn't about to be conservative about earrings.

Was I trying to be a conformist? Not really. This wasn't a sleazy ploy for some sort of gain. We had been visited by a man of God, and his humility lingered after him. We didn't want to invade his congregation. We wanted to meld into it.

Of course we were late. We were clean, and we were here and were ushered into the front seat. Despite all our efforts, I could feel the stares. We were entertainers and hadn't shed our trademarks.

But these sincere Christians had melded their convictions into their look, too. Why wear a tie? Really served no purpose. Plain shirts, many of them flannel, stayed on just as well without a tie. They looked scrubbed. Ladies looked nice. I'd never noticed styles. They just looked nice. We seemed to have stepped into a time-freeze up here. Somehow, I admired all of it. They clasped our hands, and we entered into their worship.

We met in the gym so we had no architectural

curves or gothic designs to enhance our yen to worship. The harsh rigid basketball lines of the gym were a stark reminder that our tithe would be used in a multipurpose service to the Lord. The soft hues from stained glass would come when the congregational needs had been met. The spirit of our worship service depended on the fire in the soul of the man who stood before us. Who had taken the time to visit a strange new couple and ask them to worship with them. We were here.

"I am standing on Holy Ground
And the angels seem to gather all around"

Hands were raised as they sang and a strong harmony rose from this congregation. Greater than the hunger for a taste of food was my hunger for this taste of memory -- when I first felt the forgiveness of God. Nine years old -- at the altar of The Bethel Assembly of God Church. It was real. I remembered how real it was. 'Restore the joy of my salvation' -- I prayed as they sang about Holy Ground -- 'Restore a right spirit within me.' My hand shot high with the others as we sang on. The congregation was ready for Don's message. I listened to his words confirming our Lord's grace. His power to forgive. I listened with a melted heart.

We were greeted. Introduced. We were welcomed. We were loved. We felt it. We knew it. We were hugged.

"Would you sing for us at the Grange Hall -- give your testimony?" they asked us at the door.

Frank Evens sensed our immediate need. "You know, there is a job opening at Safeway. They need someone to mop the floors in the early morning before the customers fill the store. Would you be interested?"

"Interested? I'll take it! You bet I'm interested!"

We drove up our hill feeling warm, loved, accepted and glowing within.

"I got a job Becky! It won't start for a while; I still can drive for Dad."

Dad seemed to be waiting for my call.

"Ready to start, Monday?"

Dad. Stocky, his skin had browned, he had more grey outlining his dark wavy hair than I had remembered. Would you say he was taciturn? Not really. He speaks his mind. Only says what he was blame sure was worth being said. But he was here. When you needed him, he had glue for your boat and seemed to know what made it leak.

"Just point the way, Dad, and I'll do the rest. Even fix the flats," I told him as I crawled in the car.

Mom looked as pert as ever as she tucked Dad in the back with pillows. Pushed the thermos in beside him where it leaked only its aroma of being fresh brewed. We were off.

It was autumn. And autumn has always brought out the best of the bards. I could recall their ilk as they penned their glowing verses about this time of year when the initial rite of ripening happens. I wanted to make a comparison and tell Dad how meaningful this time of his life was to me. But I was no poet and neither was he.

He knew his route well and knew his people. "Good people here. Hard working, pay their bills ... salt of the earth."

"Ya, it sure seems that way."

"Good farmers too. You know Rob, I always had a yen to be a farmer. Do what you kids are doing up on your mountain."

"You're kidding, Dad. I thought you never wanted

to be anything but a seasoned salesman. That you had to sell. They are a breed of their own, you know. You can't sell much to raccoons and squirrels. Those squirrels knew how to hop over my traps better than I knew how to set them."

"You're going to make it, Son. You're going to make it. I have faith in you. Randy is jealous of you. Wishes he had the guts to make the switch and do what you are doing, but he has limits to the amount he wants to risk."

"Honestly, do you mean that?" Even though we were talking over and around our heart feeling for each other, a sort of awe was shared between us because of the admiration we felt for each other. We didn't need to say it with words. It was good to be together. But Dad felt he had to try and explain something.

"Maybe I could have spent more time with you and Randy, Rob, but I was out on the road trying to make a living, and one just can't be in two places at one time."

"Say Dad, I never appreciated you more than when I was down by that Safeway store trying to sell that cord of wood. The guy who put food on our table and struggled to keep it there ... Boy, Dad, you're great in my eyes. Real OK, Dad. Real OK."

We talked about gardening and books we had read about it. I tried to tell him about the church service. Dad had always been a Christian for as long as I could remember. A strict, obedient, tithe-paying Christian. I mentioned the unadorned people in our little church. He said it was the only kind he felt good about.

"I know the kind. They are more concerned about the sweat on your brow than your embellishments. It's a slippery kind of world out there, and they want to stay clear of it."

We didn't talk about my episode in the basement. He had a peculiar kind of empathy. He didn't need to push himself to understand, he just did -- with a slap on the back, a quick smile, he let me know he was in my corner. He let me know how much he had come to appreciate Becky. That he'd back us. We could count on it.

You realize the volumes you want to say when you pass it off with "Good old Dad." He made his sales and finished the week with a better back, and I had money in my hand for the essentials of living on our mountain. The Safeway job started next week.

Chapter 10

BECKY

"It isn't that life up here is boring, Lord," I prayed. "It's hard. And now Rob is gone during every daylight hour. When the girls are asleep this cabin feels vacant, abandoned, empty. When Rob is home, it's our spot of challenge."

I thought Rob and I would overcome together up here, but now we were more apart from each other and more alone than ever. When I needed to tell someone that, there was no one here to listen.

I knew I hadn't discovered loneliness. Pioneer women cried out that they were lonely. Like me, they had no washing machines, but I think they had beds. The garish looking sleeping bags, left by us on the floor each morning, made me feel we had left the continent and the century.

It seemed we should have had beds by now. Didn't know that having a bed would be such a big thing. Where is my victory, Lord? When I testify about God's goodness, I mean it with all my heart. God is good. But why do I feel that sleeping on the floor is getting to be a drag? It was my choice to come here.

I know that Rob has to earn money. He's so excited about earning money that he seems garbed in heady elation, while all day I'm thinking that I'm nine miles from a neighbor or a phone.

Light from the sun that had found its way through the cloud cover had just peeked through my kitchen window. It had finally pushed back the Washington mists that hung over us this time of the year. It reminded me that somehow, everything would get done before Rob got home. I had a day ahead of me, and I'd become much better at finishing what I knew I had to do. It was just getting started that I couldn't handle.

What I needed was a jumper cable. Something that would grab and spin my motor until I could get at the wash. At least I have soap now, enough for all the clothes that were outlining the floor in piles. But it had been raining the last few days and hanging clothes on the tree boughs promised to be a slippery mess. I'd been sliding around out there, and it seemed to be getting slicker with every step.

And the flies bombarded us since the rain. Seemed to think we came up here to rescue them. I've used up the fly spray. "I'm so tired, Lord, and one glance at last night's dishes piled in the sink shows the spaghetti sauce turning to stone."

I shook the coffee pot. Maybe I'd find a genie in there that would give me the gusto I needed to get started. I reached for my cigarettes. Why do I do it? Why do I do it?

I bent over the table edge as I tapped the ash into Rob's cup of cold coffee. How could a table that was so heartwarming when we ate breakfast together, look sullen and threatening now? Like "I'll tell on you, you can't get your work done."

I thought of the Grange Hall where we sang our testimony. Folks loved us. Wanted to hear more. Rob bared his soul, giving glory to God. It was wonderful. He was so grateful and thankful and humble. Oh I hate this self-pity. Look at me. Look at me. Can't get at the wash without my cigarette.

Finally I pulled up from the table and, with my coffee cup in one hand, reached for the door. Autumn. Already it's here. The leaves that turn were tinged with the first colors of fall. Birds had started saying their good-byes in a chorus of excited, tuneless chirps because it was their destiny. Some clock within told them to go, and they were fixing to do so.

Are we fakers, Lord? I dropped my head and tears dropped into my cup. I mean my prayers. I have faith to wait for Your leading and faith to surrender to Your will. But when the day gets hot and the sink is full of last night's dishes - when the place is filled with flies - Oh Lord, I can't toss my cigarettes. What would folks think if they knew? Knew that I made Rob buy my cigarettes for me? What would they think if they knew how we fight?

Communicate? That's all I hear - we need to communicate.

We've tried that. Last week Rob tried it. "Funny," he said after we finished the fried chicken fixed the way he likes it, "you do manage to get things done in this cabin so it looks nice and home-like and smells wonderful when I get home. But when you had that lovely home in Spokane, you couldn't manage at all. Seemed you slept most all day long."

"You know perfectly well, Rob, that I had low thyroid. There were times when I could hardly lift my coffee cup to my face." As usual I started to cry.

"But even after you were taking thyroid you couldn't get at your work. I don't mean to criticize, I just mean that even though it's so much harder for you here, you're doing so great."

I couldn't be satisfied with his compliment. I had to contest his reference to our past. It hadn't been a part of our exchange.

"Rob, you know blame well why I was depressed. I knew you were seeing Rita, and it was killing me. You can't believe how it hurt me. Why did you bring it up? I'm still trying to get over her. Really, I am Rob. I pray for forgiveness, and when I think I have victory, she comes back to haunt me," I sobbed. I even screamed my words.

"I didn't bring her up!" he fought back, tossing his hands in hopelessness. "I was just trying to give you a compliment."

I knew that was true. Why did I jump on him like that? But he should know. He should know that my battle wasn't over. Even when I think it was - it wasn't.

"Rob, honestly, you can't believe how she's haunted me. How do I measure up? Do I keep house as well? She can't sing. She's not a model. But would she be better for you?"

He told me I was putting myself through needless torment. He was sorry he mentioned it.

Are we a couple of fakers, Lord? Should we even give our testimony? Should we even sing when we're not having the victory we're singing about?

Oh, if I could just get going - just get going. I inhaled deeply on the last of my cigarette. I knew what I was doing. Brother, I'd heard it enough on television.

"You mess up my lungs, mess up everyone's lungs. But, I can't quit, I need something, and you're my jumper cable," I moaned to my cigarette as I carefully hid the stub.

The wash got finished. The dishes done. The floors were wiped up with the rinse water. Rob would be home soon and the place smelled of meat loaf and baked potatoes.

Take away my cigarettes, Lord.

ROB

Every new day the Great Landscaper decorated our dwelling place. Snow was our hardship up here, but it glistened. One morning our universe would be white frosted, like the expensive Christmas trees. The next, the evergreens would have their boughs decorated with whipped icing. When the sun hit, our world danced. We were glad that our towering evergreens let the sparkles filter through rather than glare at us. We always felt dwarfed by this beauty that was morning crisp and new in design every time we awakened to it. Someone should see this. We were glad it was us.

More and more folks were asking me to speak. It humbled me and enhanced the godliness I was seeking. I remembered hearing about the congregation that had been abandoned with no pastor, so the deacons and elders took turns bringing the message. When a young minister was sent to revive the work, he found a stirring revival going on. "We live our sermons," said the deacon, "for a whole month while we're preparing it and the congregation sees to it that we live it for a month after we preach it, and by that time it's time to preach again." It works that way. I was seeking godliness with contentment.

We wanted a cow. A jersey cow. We talked about it every time we filled our glasses at the table. Rich, creamy tasting milk. I would start looking for her, and while I looked I fenced. Somewhere she was waiting for us.

The job at Safeway was buying the groceries but wasn't putting cash in our hands. The mortgage payments during the winter months loomed before me, the taxes would come due and we needed a different truck. I was cutting wood, but I was warned about the snow pile-up on our mountain. Surviving up here would be all we could expect for a couple months, they told us. Now was the time to lay-by the funds to tide over the heavy snows. An idea was grabbing me, and the more I sized up our scrawny little evergreens that grew deep in our forest the more excited I became.

"Yes, it is a wild idea!" I agreed with Becky. But think how it would challenge the creative artist that blooms only at Christmas. Anyone can hang tinsel on those perfectly clipped trees that fill the lots. My trees would be for the sensitive spirit that needs a challenge. "Grew in our woods just for you. Look at its struggle for a bit of light. Arched, bent, and even gnarled at this tender age by the adversity of nature. Just awaiting your touch."

"Help me decorate one Becky. You're the artist in this family. Give it everything you got, and we'll sell trees."

Becky didn't quite catch the excitement I felt, but she said she'd give it her best try.

Again I was starting early and coming home late.

In between making-hay at the Safeway store, I was making-hay in our forest. I shoveled snow. I tossed it, carved it and sculptured it. I marveled at it when it was soft and downy, realizing it was made up of tiny beautiful flakes. I hated it when it was so packed and hard that I nearly pulled off a boot that had sunk into three feet of it.

I marveled when drifts of snow grew to two feet, then three feet and in places four feet. But it helped me reach the tops of the trees that could be cut for Christmas trees. I'd crawl over the hard drifts with my saw and cut off the tops, which made queer little trees which I dragged to the edge of the clearing where I could load them on our truck. As I cut them, I could envision how they would look. I rehearsed my sales pitch.

November disappeared off the calendar before I noticed it. Our pile of trees was impressive. And I had found the lot. Only a garage was left of my great aunt's place at the corner of Francis near Division in Spokane, and it seemed a good spot. We set up shop to sell our trees.

Becky was fighting loneliness more than ever. She always had a good meal ready and hot and I'd be too tired to listen to the stories of her day. It worried me. Life had become a juggling act between spending so many hours working for the means of supporting my family that I had no time to spend with them. But I could not face the winter short of funds to meet our needs. I found there was such a thing as a twenty dollar handshake.

We had come to church with ten dollars. It was all we had. I had rehearsed over and over the many needs of our little family, but before the offertory we learned of the many needs of our little church. My ten dollars passed back and forth in my hands. Should I give it? I dropped it in because I had to. The tug of God to give was real. At the door, a brother who had heard Becky and I give our testimony squeezed my hand. What he squeezed into my hand was a twenty dollar bill! I am still hunting for words to tell the glory of it.

But now we had another problem. To sell trees I would have to be on the lot day and night. Becky could not stay here alone with the girls. There was only one thing to do. Mom said that Becky could stay with her while I camped out on the lot in a tent. Becky doesn't like the idea. She has curtains on the windows. The cabin is our home, and she likes to be at home with our girls. But she would do it. She would go.

"Honey." Becky approached me after devotions with that hesitant step that I had learned was a signal that she had something to say that she was afraid might be painful.

"Rob honey, I worry about Spokane." She put her arms around me as though wanting to shield me from something. "It's a whole different world out there, and you are doing so wonderful here. You won't want to go back to that bottle of wine again, will you?"

My family, my beautiful wife and our wonderful little church; go back to that bottle that almost took my life? How could she even think it?

"Of course not Becky, but I don't blame you for being concerned."

BECKY

"Oh God, where are you? We're mired under again. Rob is down at the lot selling trees like crazy and I'm here with the folks doing everything wrong."

Whatever I thought of Rob's 'ugly-tree' idea, he was proving me wrong. All last week I kept getting reports of his sales going up as well as his prices. But staying with the folks was not going that well with me, and I was telling my troubles to God.

"Whatever was wrong before - this is worse. At least I had my problems on my own turf, now it seems I'm fair game for everyone's appraisal.

"Dad is forever correcting me. I know He thinks that if I will only pull my share, Rob will pull right along with me. There's always something I should correct about my ways. But brother, I'm trying. He's beating on the wrong horse, and I'm having trouble with that." My prayers were not of praise but of gripes and pain.

"And Mom chimed in all day yesterday. Seemed I pulled enough blunders to prove I am a lousy mother. The little I've seen of Rob, I've had the feeling he is getting to think so too.

"I admit that I spanked Anja too hard. The marks I left on her little butt sure proved it. But Anja was so naughty when she started swatting at little Tasha. In one single minute, she could prove to all of them how badly I am out of control. Because I swatted her and that was something Rob's mother never approved of. She doesn't say too much but sighs a lot.

And she doesn't think I feed Tasha right. I've been pureeing her food because we have almost no money and I have no milk, so I've put a little sugar in her water to get her to drink more.

"I've never heard of anyone feeding their baby sugar water!"

"They do in the hospital."

"Well, I never heard of that!"

"Mom always gave her babies sugar water when she didn't have breast milk for them."

I felt God listened, but I wasn't sure I had a case. It seemed no matter how hard I tried, things were going kiddy-wampus.

I could sense how the folks chalked us up. Funny, on our mountain, people wanted to hear our testimony, wanted us to sing. Here, the folks wanted us to shape up fast. My folks did too. They think we've floundered around like some untrained colts. Their other kids were doing fine, but we're the ones that were hard to handle.

"Oh God. Are you about to give up on us too? Is there any hope for us? Paul says, "I know how to be abased and how to abound. Only on our mountain do we abound.

"Becky! Becky!" I didn't miss the house beautiful

gleam of having the morning work done and a coffee cake started.

"Becky, Anja has her boots on and is trying to get out the door to go see her Daddy. I'm trying to get this coffee-cake ready to go so Dad can take some of it down to Rob on the lot. It's only 17 degrees out!"

How could my dear little Anja get me in so much trouble? When I tried to get her away from the door, she kicked and screamed, and I'm not supposed to paddle? I tossed the hair out of my eyes and tried to hide the shame of my confusion. When Anja has her mind made up, nothing can distract her. I felt like giving up.

The day did not improve.

Tomorrow, Lord, I will go and help Rob on the lot, but tonight the bed is cold and empty. I miss him. I've tried repeating Bible verses, but grabbing my consciousness is that inner voice accusing me, "You are a lousy mother, you are a lousy mother." I hear it in my bones, my heart, and all my senses. I just don't want Rob to know that I'm a lousy mother.

I knew I had been carrying heart scars, and they never seemed to heal. I never knew they were there until hurts ripped them open and the aches returned with their familiar pain.

I used my sisters as yardsticks. They've had hard working husbands too, but there had been no Rita in their lives. They have homes with new carpets. Beautiful Christmas trees piled with presents heralded a season so tinseled that you were gripped with their celebration.

We've only sold trees and watched others getting ready to celebrate. I wondered if I'd get money for presents. I cried and my empty bed shook with my sobs.

I cried for my husband. I loved him.

How can I forget your love and patience," I cried to my husband's pillow. "Forget how you stood by me when I was a jailbird. When the judge pronounced the sentence, 'Six weeks in the county jail,' you were there. When everyone wanted you to shake me off your fingers, you fought for me. We were so in love. Those hard weeks behind bars? Without you, I couldn't have made it, Rob. I owe you so much.

"You were so kind, so good and loving. You showed me the love of Jesus, and together we pledged our lives to Him and to each other."

Lord, why is our walk so hard? Other Christians seem to have such a good life compared to us. For us - one problem runs into another. I grabbed his pillow and cried.

Will I ever get over this fear of losing him? This feeling that I will lose what I love the most? Will I walk with this fear of losing all my life? This fear I haven't been able to shake since Mother was killed.

Will I ever get over it? Will I always measure happiness by that hopping up and down Saturday? That somersaulting Saturday when Dad took all of us out for a ride on his new dune-buggy. It was finished and done -- he had worked on it so long. Our aunts and uncles had joined us, and we were crazy with excitement. We had our own dune-buggy! Our own dune-buggy! I knew that no one on earth was happier than I was. I remember, I sat in the back with my sisters and laughed and sang as we shot over the sand dunes. We zoomed along like sailing over clouds.

My beautiful mother was there to lift us in and kiss us when we returned. Dad was so proud. I was nine and proud of everything.

"And I remember those last words when Dad said,

"Now it's your turn, honey." I remember her last look at us as she laughed and waved and crawled in beside him. Tall, blond, beautiful. Even at that time I wanted to look like her, wanted to be like her, be as gentle a mother as she was.

But I never saw her again. She vanished. Just disappeared. I only heard about the accident and saw my father bruised and broken. I couldn't go to the funeral because they thought it best. I only saw Daddy sobbing over her picture night after night. Will I always be afraid I will lose again? Won't I ever get over it?

Lord, even though You sent us another mother, I was rebellious and bitter. And confused... She set the six of us plus her two up at a table of good food. We had a home again. She organized us, and we felt a warm feeling again when we came home from school. But my feelings confused me. How could I love her for being so good and patient with us and at the same time resent her because Daddy loved her. I couldn't trust my feelings, that they were right.

She seemed to understand, and when I was in jail for shoplifting, I realized how hard she tried to be my good mother. They came, the folks did, and stood by me. I will always want to help a kid in trouble. I know how badly they can hurt.

ROB

Christmas in Spokane was winter at its best. Poets have sung all renditions of the feeling but none like Bing Crosby who lived here. He had watched his home town light up as Christmas was coming around again, and wrapped up the feeling with his song. I never tired of the words, and they put people in a buying mood for my trees like nothing else.

"It's beginning to look a lot like Christmas
Everywhere I go"

Sometimes I whistled an obligato, hummed a harmony or joined old Bing with loud voice and sold my trees. They paid eight dollars for our ugly trees and then carted them off to their pick-ups like hugging a trophy.

I stacked the dollar bills together in bunches of twenty and slid the box under my cot. I pondered a bit about the greed of old Ebenezer. Those dollars felt too good in my fingers. I knew they shouldn't feel all that good.

I read my Bible and prayed as I stashed those dollars away. *"I will not forget Your lessons, Lord."* Constantly, I worried that I might forget our hard learned lessons. I vacillated between a heartfelt praise to my Lord for this provision for our needs and a heady giddiness when I watched people teasing each other about falling for my sales-pitch.

"You too," they'd laugh as they met their neighbors going through our trees ...

"Sure, why not," a wife would laugh as her breath billowed around her like a steam engine. "It's what I always wanted - an ugly tree."

"George," a fellow would call to his neighbor, "you know, I often wondered why a good looking gal like Alice would pick an old goat like you. She's got the 'ugly-tree syndrome' in her blood."

"Ya, I s'pose. Wondered about that myself," Old George would answer as he struggled to dig under his mackinaw and sweater for his wallet. "But I swear your

Elsie is sizing up a tree a lot uglier than what I got here."

They bought my trees.

My old tent was feeling better all the time. A donation from Dad. With a barrel stove in the middle that I kept hot from the broken evergreen boughs I burned, the place was warm and the smell of the burning pine was exhilarating.

Conversation is the same the world over. Weather. "Have you heard of the snow piling up in the North woods?"

"North?" I asked the customer. "You mean north, like Cheweleh?"

"Brother," he laughed. "It's been piling up in them woods up there about three feet deep since December.

"You can plan to be snowed out of your woods," they kept telling me, "until about April — even May maybe. Any trees you intend to get out of your woods you better have gotten out by now."

"Snowed out of your woods." That sure wrecked my plans for the coming weekend. I was running out of trees and our last and biggest weekend was coming up. I needed more trees, and I couldn't get into the woods to cut them.

Where do people get their trees? I walked my finger through the ads and found one that looked like a possibility.

"We need to head for home," said a congenial voice that I learned was from Montana. "Have a bunch of Alpines on this lot in Moses Lake, and we just aren't doing too good. People seem to want those full clipped Spruce that the lots are full of these days. If you take the whole bunch, I'll let you have them for two bucks a piece."

"Two bucks a piece! I'll take them."

I sat on my cot figuring out how I'd stretch that cache under my bed to last from January to May. Have to pay the mortgage six months in advance. Lay by a six month's supply of food. Our seventy-five dollar truck was treating every trip through the snow like it would be its last. I had to get a new truck. And I needed a bigger power saw if I was going to make time cutting bigger trees.

I was to learn that Becky had a list of her ideas for spending that money too.

Chapter 12

BECKY

"Honey, I'm here!" Whatever were my complaints about living with Mom and Dad, they always told me they'd take care of the girls if I wanted to visit Rob on the lot. I had to find a time when I could get a ride as Rob had taken the truck with him.

The lot was crowded with people. I couldn't believe it. Folks were joking, and Rob was laughing with them over his ugly trees. He was bringing in the cash to hide under the bed.

"I can't believe this Rob! I admit I thought it was a hairbrained idea, but you sure proved me wrong. My man is quite a salesman!" I purred in his ear as I hugged him. "Has it been like this all the time?"

The lot was almost empty of trees except for the few picked over scragglers leaning on each other in the corners. Folks had beaten down the snow until the lot looked like a hi-low shag carpet that for a long time had needed a scrubbing. Even the picked over scragglers were going.

The tent had the feel of being where the action was. I sat on the cot and felt the pulse of waiting for the money to come in. Rob kept the fire roaring in the stove which kept his coffee pot jiggling and dancing. The pungency of his fresh brew was gripping; it set a tempo of energy about the place.

Rob brought in a huge steaming pizza that we cut and pulled apart, twirling the pieces to catch all the melted cheese. Everything made us giddy and glad to be together.

I was glad that the job was almost done. We would clean up the yard, count our horde and go shopping. I had made out the list. The closer it is to Christmas the more exciting it is to shop. Oh, it would be a great Christmas!

"Rob, you have done so well - I know how tired you are. Aren't you glad that it's over?" I enthused to his back. He was bent over, filling the heater with wood.

"We'll do so much better next year, Hon!" I egged on his efforts. "Now we know they want your crazy trees. Oh, I'm so proud of you, you've worked so hard!" I twisted his hair around my fingers and he kept piling bough after bough in the heater.

"Now, we can celebrate our first Christmas on our mountain. Aren't you glad you're finished?"

Rob ran out to take care of a customer sizing up the trees that were left. I was amazed as I watched him. He was waving his arm over the lot and the customer nodded his head and crawled in his car. He didn't make a sale.

"That's OK Rob, those last trees will make good firewood." I grasped his shoulders to look into his eyes. "You sure came through with your idea. I won't ever doubt you again. I can't wait to wrap it all up and get back to our mountain. I'm so lonesome for that place."

He didn't turn to me. Instead he went out for more fir branches. He kicked the snow off them and shook them good before bringing them in. Painstakingly he shook the branches even when there wasn't a speck of snow left on any needle. I knew he was stalling for time. What was he hating to tell me?

"Becky, we're not finished!" he said at last while he was piling them in the woodbox he had fashioned from an orange crate. "I just bought out a bunch of Alpines from a fellow who has a lot in Moses Lake. There's a couple there from Montana who need to get back home."

"Rob, you didn't! You couldn't have!" I screamed. "Didn't you even see the trees? You've just gotten heady now after selling this bunch. You mean you're throwing all this good money after a bunch of no-good trees?"

I was aiming my words like bullets. Didn't he know what he was doing? Finally, we've made some money so we could buy some of the things we needed so badly. Finally, I could take my girls home to a Christmas on our mountain, and he's going to throw all our money after that fellow's no-good trees.

"That fellow most likely can't sell those trees, Rob!" I screamed my words and punctuated my screams with tears and clenched fists. "He most likely can't sell those Alpines, and he has the good sense to hightail it back where he came from.

"Rob! Rob! You didn't!"

I couldn't believe he'd do that. Why couldn't we be satisfied with our good fortune? We had done so much better than I had ever dared to hope.

"Rob, can't we go shopping for a few things like everyone else is doing? I can't even bear to go up town anymore and watch everybody with their arms full of presents for someone and I can't buy a thing."

"Will you quit comparing us to everybody else? We're not like everyone else!" he shouted at me. My mild mannered husband was shouting. He never does that. I shout but not him.

"No, I can't believe this!" I repeated myself over and over. I sobbed. "I've been staying with your folks so we could make some money and now you're spending it for someone else's Alpines! Rob, I can't believe this."

"Becky, do you think I enjoy doing this any better than you do? Do you think I like being the scrooge that denies my family a Christmas?" He dinked around the stove. Poured out the coffee to start a new brew. He did everything but look at me.

"Be reasonable," he pleaded. "The biggest weekend of the year for Christmas trees is coming up. I'm snowed out of our woods so I can't cut any more, and I have to get trees. I've found a way, Becky! I've found a way!" His voice broke as though I had pushed him to the limit. I felt ashamed but then, I reasoned, I cry all the time.

"I sure thought you would be reasonable about it." He continued talking to his stove. "Hard to believe you'd act like this."

I threw myself on the bed and sobbed. I couldn't worry about being reasonable. I was too heartbroken. It wasn't as though we didn't have money. We had lots of money under the bed.

"Have you ever heard of the 'Gift Of The Magi?" I shouted at him. "That husband sold his heirloom watch to get combs for his wife's hair. That guy had his priorities straight!" I knew that I had hurt him. And that was what I wanted to do. If the tent flap would have slammed, he would have slammed it as he ran out on the lot.

I was glad I had said it and a bit guilty that I hurt him. After I had waited and waited to come down to the lot to see him, I had blown it. But all he thinks about is buying more trees! He hasn't even thought about our Christmas.

I figured out what he was doing with that last customer. He was promising that guy that he would have new trees next week, that's what he was doing. He does fully intend to buy those trees.

He slipped back into the tent and came over to the cot to put an arm around me. "Becky, let's try and talk this over once more." He had been outside rehearsing his reasons and felt I was entitled to an accounting.

"It's the snow, Becky. All I've been hearing is how we're going to be snowed in on our mountain and snowed out of our woods. I won't be able to get into town to work at the Safeway. There will be no money coming in for six months. And making money to provide for you guys is my responsibility." He sat up and wiped his forehead. The heater was getting hot.

"No money coming in." I listened. I was not forgetting the squirrels jumping over our traps. Even the Israelites didn't have a faucet of cool water waiting for them. They had to dig their own wells.

"We need to pay the mortgage for six months. We have to set by food for six months. And I have to get a different truck or I won't get my firewood off our place. You remember how it nearly busted in two Thanksgiving day, and ever since that welding job I haven't known how long it will hang together.

"And I need a bigger power saw." He continued his account of where our money should go. "I've been doing a lot of thinking, Becky, and it's the only way I can think of making it through the winter."

With reasons like that, quitting now and spending the money on Christmas seemed very frivolous. We'd buy the trees.

"Rob! I screamed, "Fire! There's a fire!" I was under the bed grabbing for our money box.

A spark from the fire had ignited the branches he had carried in and in seconds the flame was reaching for the top of our tent.

Rob yelled and grabbed the milk carton setting on our counter. He aimed and spurted the milk at the flames. The stench was sickening but it doused the fire. I had mixed emotions but knew I must thank God that we hadn't burned down. We must get those trees so Rob could make the money he knew we needed for the winter ahead. I told him how wonderful he was. And I meant it.

ROB

"Back! Back! — Over." I signaled to my Montana friend who was moving his truckload of trees into my lot. Becky didn't say a word as I counted out $800.00 into his hand, three fourths of everything we had made.

"Good luck," he said. We cinched the deal with a handshake. He was honest and didn't want us to get rooked. He hadn't sold a tree. But he let us have them for two bucks a piece, and one couldn't cut and haul them for that.

The atmosphere was icy. Becky was letting me know she wouldn't wager any bets that those trees would sell. Despite our good luck with our homegrown trees, parting with the money under the bed hadn't come easy.

She coughed a lot. And she hadn't looked at our Montana buddy even when talking to him.

I could tell that Hal wasn't feeling too comfortable. No decent fellow wants to unload his lemons on another guy's beautiful wife, so his sense of good will got a boost when three cars pulled into the lot.

"See you got those trees you were talking about."

"Yeah, we just have to unload them and you can see for yourself how ugly they are."

"Well, you ain't just a kidding. You know you started something around here. Anyone who amounts to anything in these parts has to pick up an ugly tree these days. What do they say? 'It makes a statement.' Something like that, I guess."

"How much do you want for this misfit?" asked one of the buyers spinning the little misshapen alpine from its top.

"Looks pretty good to me," I countered. "How about fourteen dollars?"

"Fourteen dollars!" shouted my customer. "Hasn't your price gone up? Seems you were selling them for around eight bucks a couple of weeks ago."

"A couple a weeks ago they weren't near as ugly."

"You can say that again," he laughed and counted out the dollars in ones. And so did the other two fellows who drove in behind him."

"Well, I'll be!" Hal gasped. "I can hardly believe this! At least now I don't feel guilty. More like mad. Why didn't I think of a gimmick like that!"

"Well, you heard of the pet rock. Seems to work that way, my friend. Maybe folks like to blow it on something they don't really need once in a while," I guessed, as Hal closed the door of his truck.

Already I liked him a lot and was sure we would be good friends. "I'll see you in Montana next year. Be up for more ugly trees." I had the feeling that he drove off feeling both good and bad.

Becky spent time on the lot and chipped in to help. She didn't spare herself, but she was bossy. I didn't think I had done too badly with my trees. Wasn't that keen on moving them around on the lot for better display purposes. They weren't selling because of their location or the way they were displayed anyway. They were selling because they were ugly.

She wanted to rearrange the tent. Clean it. Rake the tree lot. Keep better books.

It was her adjectives that bugged me. Too many things were "stinkin." We had to have an ice chest for the milk and baloney, even though we ate everything we brought in and tossed the rest to the birds. Strange how I felt her touch made our mountain home rich, beautiful and full of feeling. Here, I was ashamed to admit, her efforts seemed more like an intrusion.

And we still fought over money. She reminded me every day about the washer and the porch steps. I kept telling her I was going to get to them, but it was my responsibility to bring home food for my family, and I had to have the means of doing it. I felt she was comparing me to my brothers-in-law.

She seemed convinced that I was a scrooge who didn't care about her wants. That was not true. Her wants were all I cared about. But six months on that mountain with no income! I thought about that too. Just when I had it figured out on paper how we would make it, she would tell me of all the things she really couldn't do without much longer.

MAKING IT: SELLING WOOD

FIXING UP WHAT OTHERS LEFT BEHIND

"I'LL FIX UP THAT PLACE"

MOM & DAD BRINGING FOOD.

And she would tell me about all the ways her family had always celebrated Christmas. Strange that this hadn't been an issue with us before. Becky had always done her Christmas shopping and gift exchanging without involving me all that much. Now it had become a crisis. And what really hurt, was that it should matter that much, when food on our table was our major priority, but it made me sell my ugly trees for better prices all the time. Some brought in as much as twenty-five dollars. I kept piling the dollars under the bed.

I began asking about trucks. A bigger truck was a necessity. I was getting an education for my future in the woods; the truckers knew the ropes. And there wasn't much they enjoyed more than conditioning a greenhorn for the ways of a mountain man. One thing was certain - I must get a better saw.

But Becky had a one track mind. "They're starting to cut prices before Christmas, Rob. That's the time Mom always did most of her shopping for us kids."

"Of course, Becky, I know how important it is to you."

"I'll really be careful, Rob."

"I know you will - take what you need, Becky."

I felt mean when I saw the few dollars she took from the box. I would have to learn to balance my concerns. Maybe I over learned the lessons I starved to discover before I sold my first cord of wood beside the Safeway Store.

We were doing better on these trees than I had dared to hope. I must loosen up. I must honor what is important to Becky. She wants a Christmas for our children, like she had when she was a kid.

The trees sold - almost all of them. We had

$3,000.00 for the winter days ahead. We didn't get up to our mountain for Christmas as our biggest rush on the lot was on Christmas Eve. Mom fixed a great dinner for us Christmas day. We visited Becky's folks and her sisters. They all had presents for us. I finally noticed that Becky was right. They knew how to celebrate Christmas. Visited Randy, and he had presents for us too.

I shared in the pain of giving the small tokens that Becky had picked out for everybody. She had wanted to give so much more.

"Next year we will do much better," I kept promising her after every visit. Where had I been that I hadn't noticed how important this part of living was to my wife.

Right now I was grateful that I would be able to keep my promise to her. I could hear myself repeating it all day and would wake up at night repeating it. "I'll keep food on this table - I promise."

We were making plans for our New Year and very anxious to get back on our hill. I had been looking for a truck, taking down the tent and cleaning up the yard. I was sweeping up the broken evergreens when Rick, my old singing buddy, came by.

"Say Rob, we sure do miss you on the job these days." His long hair and leather pants were as familiar as yesterday. His warm grip on my shoulder told me that he meant what he said. I had been missed. The spot I left behind had not been filled.

"You know, Rob," he continued, "there's not anything that would make all of us feel better this New Year's Eve than having you sing for us tonight."

"I'd sure like to, Rick." I remembered the buddies we used to be, the back slaps that we gave each other that meant more than a hundred words. The cup of coffee he'd bring me when the eyelids were drooping, or the cough drops he always had on hand to clear the rasp out of a raw throat ... we had become each other's prop for a windy day.

"I'd better spend New Year's Eve with Becky," I said.

"I can understand that, old Buddy. Sure I can. But couldn't you just sing one song? Then you could run home to Becky and watch the New Year in.

"You sure know how to make me do just that, Rick. Can I think it over? If I can work it out I'll come. OK?"

"Good! Good! You know they've been saying that you've gotten pretty religious. They call you "The Monk". Say you're working it out on your "Mountain Monastery". I'd sure like to let them see that you are still, good ole Rob."

I mentioned it to Becky when I got home. "You can't believe who came to the lot today. Rick wants me to sing just one song for them tonight."

Becky may have had her misgivings, but she didn't mention them. She and Mom had been making plans for New Years. Because the mountain would be snowed in, they would get Dad to take us out to eat, and I would get the place plowed out.

We decided that I'd drive out tonight and find someone to plow out our yard tomorrow morning.

Great Idea. I'd sing my song tonight and drive home to get the place manicured before they got there.

It was going to be a great year.

I tried praying about singing that song. But I hadn't been praying much this last month. Mostly, I had been falling into bed from exhaustion and thanking God that the dollars were piling up under it. Mostly I had been thanking God on the run, not praying for His day by day guidance.

"Grieve not The Spirit that is within thee." The thought troubled me, but I couldn't tell if the tormenting uneasiness I felt was the normal uneasiness one feels when taking a chance. Or was I grieving The Spirit? I had felt uneasy when paying $800.00 for the trees, too.

The fellows were belting out the lyrics when I pushed open the door, and they didn't seem all that bad. I remembered how we tried to placate our conscience when we took the job. "We'd be a light in a dark place." Maybe I could be that tonight.

They started clapping when I pushed open the door.

Hey! Hey! Hey! Now what - d - ya say.
Would ya look who stumbled out our way.

They clapped me right up to sing. The song I was to sing was very strange, but it had a message of sorts if they had given me a chance to explain them.

"I want a new drug," I sang. Not one that deserts you in the morning and leaves you to face the world alone and in agony. I wanted to tell them what I had found, but their welcome was overwhelming.

They clapped when I sang, and they clapped when I finished. I found myself scanning a familiar corner for a familiar face. The corner where I used to find Rita.

The music, the clapping, the smells of the bar, the handshakes, the pats on the back - they all brought back an element of my life that I thought I had wiped out of my memory. If she had been there I would have been reliving a slice of my past.

Wonder where she keeps herself? How's she getting on? There was no one I'd dare trust with that question. Would it be such a sin just to find out what became of her? I pass her place on the way home. Should I? Shouldn't I?

I almost wished for an act of destiny that would stop my truck. I slowed as I came to her street. My foot touched the brake as though it were detached from my conscience. The truck stopped.

I held my finger at her doorbell wondering what one little push would unleash ... I would always be haunted by what happened to her. Does she still live here? What did happen to her? That was all I wanted to know.

I pushed the button.

And I held my breath.

A rush of emotion pulsated a heartbeat in my ear when I heard her stirring to answer the bell.

Chapter 13

BECKY

It's over Lord, finally ... seemed like the tree project would never end. They tell us our mountain is snowed in so the only way we can make it out there would be for Rob to go home tonight and get it plowed out tomorrow. Rob is singing tonight, Oh Lord, help us now!

I've prayed all through the day. Everything's packed. I've been washing all day and cleaning up the Christmas mess between the loads. Thank goodness for plastic bags - all the Christmas gifts made going home take more room.

But I'm having a hard time, Lord. Rob's going back to sing ... can't keep my mind on what I'm doing. Oh, I'll be glad to get back on our mountain. This is Rita's turf, and I can't forget it ... Will he be strong enough to resist the temptation to see her?

Mom has been reminding me all day of what I'm forgetting. Rob's mackinaw and boots in the hall closet. Anja's vitamins in the refrigerator door. I wish I could shake my thoughts and function better.

I got the bags lined up in the halls. The girls had their baths and were so excited about going home tomorrow that I thought they'd never settle down even though Grandma read through most of their books twice.

Oh Lord, wouldn't it be awful, now that we have the money to make it through the winter, to have something happen. Something that might mess up everything we have to do on our mountain.

Oh God, help us. Help us now.

ROB

"Well! ... she said at last, leaning on the door she opened. "You're about the last thing I expected to see tonight! She didn't smile nor was her tone icy and mean. She just said what she meant to say. She hadn't expected to see me again.

"Can I come in, Rita?" She nodded but made no effort to make me feel welcome.

"Why not? I guess you can. You must have some reason for coming." She closed the door and locked it.

"I just wanted to see how you were getting along. Ask about the kids."

"You mean that's why you came?" She motioned me to the couch and pointed to my usual spot. "Would you be happy to know I'm getting along pretty stinkin bad?" I moved the ruffled green pillow, like I always did, and sat next to the arm rest. It felt like it was my spot. It was where I always sat at her place.

Nothing had changed. She mechanically measured some coffee into the coffee-maker and very slowly slid unto the far end of the couch. That was all that was different.

Where she sat. Now we would talk across the space between us on her couch.

"How did you expect I would be getting along, Rob?"

"Did you go back to your husband, Rita? "

"Do you notice any rings on my finger?"

"I'm sorry. I really am, Rita."

"You mean you came back to tell me you're sorry that I didn't get it together with my husband? That you and Becky are doing just great on that mountain? That you got religion and all I have to do is try religion and everything will be alright for me? Is that what you came to tell me, Rob?"

"Well, yes. I mean, no." Neither answer seemed wrong or right.

"What did you come to tell me, Rob?" Her voice broke. It was not like her to cry. She pulled back, dropped her head into her arm that cradled her edge of the couch. The room was icy silent. It was not a good idea that I come.

"Haven't you been seeing anyone?" I asked her. I could feel her loneliness.

"Should I? I don't want to go that route again. I'm a loser, Rob. I lost my husband. I lost you. What makes you think my luck would change. You see, I don't have much going for me. Becky is beautiful. She can sing. Actually she could get most anyone. About all I can do, Rob, is applaud, like clapping for you, having faith in you that you could make it as a singer."

"Rita, I wasn't rating the two of you against each other on a scale of 1-10. Becky is my wife, don't you see? It's never the will of God that a man should leave his wife for someone else."

"I wish you'd thought of that before I fell in love with you.

"Rob, you can't begin to know what lonely is. You can't begin to know how lucky you are. You could drop me and you have a gorgeous wife waiting for you with open arms. It's just not like that for me." She began to sob her words.

"Becky has a wedding ring, Rob,." she continued, holding out her hand to me. "You don't know what a wedding ring would mean ... Do you remember how often we talked of getting married? Do you see how empty my fingers are?" I held her hand, and ached to take her in my arms.

"Rob," she sobbed, "all I have are your tapes. I've played them over and over. Even if I couldn't have you, I had your voice. But the words were no longer for me, and they became hollow, like a voice echoing in an empty house."

I reached over for her and she sobbed on my shoulder ...

I left the truck at the road and waded through the hip high snow up to our cabin. Plowed through the snow on the porch and kicked it away from the door. The icicles hung almost to the ground around the cabin. I had to break them off to get the door open. Never had I been in a place so terribly cold. And I didn't have the heart to warm it up. I had sinned. Oh God, I had sinned.

After all the Lord had taught me in this place ... after all His blessing on our undertaking ... I had sinned. Was there any hope for me? I cried my remorse. Did I deliberately sin, Lord? Is there any forgiveness for me? I crawled under all the quilts I could find and sobbed my repentance to God. Should I give up on my self? Thoughts of ending the pain seared through my thinking again and again, but finally I fell asleep.

How long I slept I don't know. I was awakened by a weird sound in the yard. Couldn't make it out - neither could I see where it came from. Almost like a rhythmical struggle for breath by an animal - that's how it sounded ...

Where did it come from? The breathing sounds turned into long wheezing gasps. I ran outside to find Dad tipped over a snowdrift!

"Dad! Dad! What in the world? ... let me help you in!

I lifted him to his feet, and we struggled in together. I made a fire; put on the teakettle for coffee.

"Dad, for goodness sake, are you alright?"

He nodded and raised his hand to pat my back. "Are you alright, Son?" he gasped. "Never - saw - anybody - work - harder - than - you - did. Had - to - see - if - you're alright ...

No other words had to be spoken. We hugged each other. He patted my back long and hard as though trying to get his words into my soul. He did. He cared so much. And I knew he knew.

Funny how men can't find words for each other. He just about died in a snowdrift to get to me and then couldn't find any words.

I remembered the verse ... If your earthly father knows how to give good gifts to his children ... how much more does your Heavenly Father ... I could go on.

BECKY

I forgave him!

Despite the advice of the books I had read; that to forgive and forgive makes you a victim that becomes an enabler to a character weakness and encourages repetition of the act; I would take my chances. I had faith in our mountain monastery. I had faith in the work of God.

Didn't I have much to learn too? Didn't I have character weaknesses? Rob took his chance with me. Against all advice, he married me. I knew he loved me.

Together, we would learn the discipline of God on this mountain.

I knew what he had done when I first stepped out of the car. The cry lines on his half frozen cheeks told the story better than he could confess it.

We arrived about two o'clock in the afternoon, and he had gotten the place cleared of snow. He didn't run to meet us or whirl me in a welcome like he often did up here. He just looked at me questioningly as his eyes filled with tears.

All my plants had frozen. The warm place we left hadn't shed its icicles yet. The dust had rolled into the corners, and our old neighbors had moved in again. They had left their tracks.

I was learning something about myself. It's times like this that I met head-on. They didn't buckle me. But trying to push myself through a dragging day - I needed my cigarettes. And my bouts with depression, my anger at fate - they still plagued me. Yes, I had much to overcome up here,

We must look to the hills together, this man I loved and me.

"How about dinner at the Parkside Inn?" Dad suggested.

I took Rob's hand and looked long into his eyes. "How about it, honey?"

We couldn't drop each other's hand. It caught Dad's eye and seemed to melt him. It was something that set the spirit for the New Year. Mom caught it too. A melted heart before the Lord. It seemed we all shared in it.

ROB

But now we must live with New Years Eve.

Becky had been so quick to forgive, but a battle of doubt was surging through her. I had rocked her trust. I saw it in her eyes. When they locked into mine they misted when no words would come. When a tight squeeze on my arm or my shoulder seemed to be saying 'I want to trust you once again'.

I could not shake the feeling that I had put a crack in the whole armor of God. "Put on the whole armor of God that ye may withstand" . . . Withstand? That mean there will be distractions. Recreation or desperation, God seems to allow no excuses, even for amateurs. The fiery darts of the devil? He expected me to withstand.

Why do I fall? Christians about me seem victorious with much less effort. Is there something wrong with me? Some character flaw that others don't have? Won't the whole armor of God work for me?

Homespun sayings crowded my thinking. They came with some thing like a bit of comfort. Someone must have been in my spot before, to even have the thoughts. "You run around a pit, you're going to fall in - "

"Run around a pit" - was that my trouble? - I thought just that once, I could play it close to the edge. I could take the chance.

How about that guy who ran around the pit - he must have done some running to get so blame wise. What happened after he fell in that pit? Did he have a Becky that looked in his eyes with forgiveness but with a hurt so deep she couldn't find words for it.

The sheltering snow around our cabin seemed a sort of barricade from the wiles of the devil. It felt safer here in our isolation.

Will I ever be prepared for the front line again?

The snow kept coming and brought its own challenge. The natives knew their winters and they also knew their mountains. "You never fight a mountain," they told us, "because you'll never win."

Your plan for survival was not unlike a plan for battle. You lay-by food and fuel. Like old Kutazov in "War and Peace," you retrench.

For Becky and me, we needed this season. The snow walls that encased our living space were not unlike the barricades thrown up against an invader.

We were not hibernating, we were retrenching and preparing for the battle for our souls. And our spirits. Others had said "they looked up so they could look in" ... we would too. For insights implanted by the Holy Spirit Both Becky and I believed that.

We prepared. Number one was food. We did that at a one time stop at Costco. The truck-like carts were heaped with every shape of can. Beans and Beets, every kind of vegetable. Fruits of all colors. Syrup, yeast, flour, salt. Peanut Butter. As Becky's point finger ran down the list, we dreamed of better ways of doing it.

"Next year, Rob honey, we'll have that Jersey cow you're always talking about, and we won't have to use stuff like this." She tossed some cartons of powdered milk on the mound stacking upon our cart.

"Eggs?" I asked. "How can we store eggs for three months until we get to a store again? Kind of scary when you think of it isn't it?"

"Naw. We'll manage, Rob honey. We'll store eyes like we store milk. Haven't you heard of powered eggs? But I'd rather store them in the hen. Rhode Island Reds - good brown eggs. You've been talking about chickens, Rob." She was off to the next aisle to add to our horde.

She stopped at the aisle packed with cigarettes. Sheepishly she glanced at me. I had read that cigarettes was worse than the addiction of alcohol. I knew she was fighting, and I knew she would overcome.

I nodded. "I understand Becky."

She was not without plans for the months and years ahead. A place where company could sit when they called on us was a must. We bought a Costco couch for $75.00 and headed for home.

"Lord we made it! We almost put the words to a melody. Money for the mortgage payments until May.

And there was money for Brutus and a used power saw, with $300.00 left in the bank to finance us until May."

It was almost a cause for celebration when we found Brutus and drove him off the car lot. The two and a half ton Chevie Mack truck seemed a mighty power on our mountain. We got him for $600.00 plus the trade in on of our old truck - our poor little truck had finally groaned its last. Becky promptly named him Brutus. It was great to watch those massive tires grab the snowdrifts and move. He took on a personality and became a sort of armor that would fend for us and help us make it through the winter.

"We made it! We made it! I fell to my knees in gratitude to God. Now I could keep my promise to Becky. "There will be food on our table."

As I walked around in the cold stillness of the morning I looked at what winter had done to our cathedral. I noted the chandelier - sparkle without a stir of anything until a single chickadee began the one song given to him by his creator.

The storm door banged. Becky ran down the steps to join me. She stopped and stepped back to survey what I was having trouble describing.

We were both humbled by the experience of having lived together in this place. As though two pilgrims of eternity were watching the silent working of their Creator while crying out for the power of His transformation in their lives.

No wonder people call her gorgeous, I thought. She looked stunning in her blue jacket against the pristine whiteness. Suddenly she laughed and ran to me.

"Rob honey, we made it! We made it" She held me

with her hug and looked past my shoulder as though uncertain as to how she would say what she seemed intent on saying.

"Rob, I have to ask you to forgive me. I never thought you could do it. Honestly, I didn't. That 'ugly tree thing' seemed the craziest idea you ever have had, and you seemed to be coming up with a crazy idea everyday," She lowered her head as her eyes misted.

"I know I fought you in everything. I know I did. Remember when I told you, 'You're forever kicking a dead dog, Rob. Don't you ever have enough sense to know when to quit. " How can you forgive me for the way I fought you when you bought those Alpines? To think you sold every one! Oh Rob!"

Oh God, is this how we start again? By forgiving each other. Our faces were buried in the warmth of each other on this cold new morning on our mountain.

"Rob honey," Becky laughed mischievously, "will we ever forget our last Thanksgiving?"

"Never Becky. That was one time I thought my idea was pretty hair - brained. When I was sitting in the cab of our old pickup with its nose pointing to the sky, I was sure the old thing had snapped in two. Ya, that sure was one bad moment."

"How did you ever get out of that cab, Rob. You know we've never talked about our adventures since we started this tree thing, honey."

"I know, and this is going to change, Becky. Actually I pushed and prayed to get that cab door open and then slid down the side of the cab and started off for the telephone that was five miles down the road."

We leaned over Brutus and help hands as we pieced the story together. How the blinding snow was drifting over the road.

"Rob honey, you know your Mom was wonderful. Dad was gone, so when she got the call, she ordered the tow truck, knowing she'd have to pay for it. We bundled up the kids and took off.

"You looked like a walking stick Rob, Actually you did, just like a walking stick when we found you." She grabbed my jacket lapels and our cold cheeks melted against each other.

"I really knew then, the bulldog tenacity of the man I married, honey."

I hugged the girl I married as if I could never let her go.

Chapter 15

BECKY

"I am disappointed with our Bible study, Rob. Why do I do this? Now, when we both want to struggle through our problems, I really get upset. I know I was the one to suggest that we start in Genesis and read through, but all I find is law, law, law. It does nothing for me, Rob honey."

We were sitting by the table with our Bibles. Very quickly we learned there was bedlam in a disorganized morning and found it would be easy to spend the whole day keeping up with the activities of surviving this winter. So we planned our day around our Bible study.

The alarm was set to ring at dawn. Rob would shovel off the night's new snow and carry in the water while I dressed the children and started breakfast. He packed the wood-box and stacked extra wood along the wall for a blizzard. He always prepared for a blizzard. There was a lot of hustle in our efforts to meet the deadline we had set for ourselves. I would set my yeast mix for the day's baking, put the boiler on for the wash, settle the children with their colors or rag dolls and we were ready to study.

We prayed for holiness. "More holiness give me," we sang as our prayer, often on our knees, and then we'd read Genesis. I was brutally honest with my teacher. If I didn't feel holy I wasn't going to pretend.

"Rob, I get angry with Abraham. He wasn't fair to Hagar. He really wasn't, Rob."

Rob was patient. He treated my comments as significant. Took notes so he could look up better answers.

"The old testament is not instant devotion, Becky. We can't just open it and read our portion for the day and feel the warm blessing of God that we seek. Besides, God didn't spare His heroes. He hung up their weaknesses for all to see. He had confidence in His ways, that they were right and just, and let us see how man tussled with them ...

"I know, I understand that, Rob. But most people seem to get a blessing by just reading a portion of scripture. Seem to find a verse that they can use in their testimony. I wish that would happen to me."

"You know something, Becky, we shouldn't be surprised at our cry for more understanding. I remember the apostle Paul saying something about it. He had nothing to do in prison but sit and meditate on the ways of God and still he cried out, 'Oh the heights and the depths of the wisdom of God. How unsearchable are His judgements and His ways past finding out.' I'm going to trust His unsearchable judgements, Becky, and pray for wisdom for His ways."

I awakened with that answer running through my thinking. What did I want from God's word ... a road map? Should I rather be praying with David - "Renew a right spirit within me?" I surprised Rob the next morning with that question. He was pleased that our Bible study was following my thoughts through the day.

As the days of January wore on, I was amazed at how much I was learning from Rob. He was studying and reading more than I found time to do. He read the Bible through and was looking up answers. He spent much time with Spurgeon, reread his Harvard Classics, and was very impressed by the pamphlets written by Keith Green.

We felt an urgency of time. As soon as the weather broke, he would have to get back in the woods. Our meager bank account was sliding close to double digit zero, and we had a long way to go in our crash course on holiness.

"What does God mean about idols, honey?" I asked Rob. "Page after page, He condemns the worship of idols. Does He mean figurines?"

"I think idols can be any hold on our consciousness. Certainly our pride. Even our singing. You know Becky, I don't want to sing until I'm purged of all pride. Of everything that stands between me and my Savior. 'He must increase but I must decrease.' I think that is the premise of the Word of God."

"Becky," he continued with his left hand holding His Bible open while he punctuated his thoughts with his preaching hand. "It's good to know that other Christians have been where we are. They seemed to have left a road map for us in their songs. Some morning, let's just read through the old hymns. The Christians before us were crying out to God for more holiness too. "Have Thine own way, Lord. Have Thine own way!" Sometimes, I have the feeling that some Christians today think that means a turn in the road, a job, an insurance policy against poverty. But you and I know it means holiness."

After a few days of morning study, I had to admit to my husband, "Rob, you know, I really believe that this reading of the old testament is doing something for me. It's giving me a mind committed to learning what pleases God." I meant that totally.

The thought of what pleases God affected my preparations for getting our family ready for regular church attendance again. We had Brutus now to help make it through the drifts that had been piling up in our driveway.

Dress after dress came off the hanger and was piled on the bed for scrutiny as I probed for guidance. Too short! Too revealing! They would have to go. I wouldn't sell them. It didn't seem right.

"Rob, I know we have no money, but I'll have to find something to wear. You've been saying we should go back to church and we must. We haven't shown up there since before Thanksgiving. I simply can't wear these dresses, honey. Do you think we might find something at a yard sale?"

"Let's give it a try, Becky."

Rob had to put the double chains on Old Brutus to get us down the hill. Then he'd have to take them off so we could travel on the gravel road and he'd have to put them back on to make it up our driveway. Both procedures were not done without explosions of ferocious expletives - followed by most sincere prayers for forgiveness as he rubbed his skinned and bleeding knuckles. I wondered if God made allowances for unplowed roads. Were Christians on plowed road better Christians or less sorely tried?

We did make it to the yard sale. The lady was three inches shorter than I was so her dresses were no help, but she did have a lovely, almost new, blue curtain.

I held it up and Rob agreed it would be beautiful. I got it for 50 cents. Also bought socks for the girls that were too large. Some had holes in the toes. These Mountain people threw away nothing. There would always be a resourceful someone - and today, that was me.

"But you don't have a sewing machine, Becky."

"I'll sew by hand. I can do that while you read the Bible."

It was having no pattern that presented a problem. How could I get it to fit around the neck without puckers? And the sleeves. How are they cut with just enough fullness in the back and enough material cut away in the front for that perfect blouse fit? I just can't afford to ruin this curtain or I'll have no dress at all.

I got an idea. Those dresses I had chucked to be discarded - at least they would give me a neck and a sleeve pattern.

I pulled them out of the bag and picked out one with pattern potential. After I ripped it apart carefully and ironed out the seam lines, I had a professional pattern. I found that a small running stitch made with double strand thread made a strong seam, and it went fairly fast.

In the evenings, after the youngsters were sleeping, Rob and I pulled up to our heating stove and let the winter happen to us. When the snow beat its hard pellets on our windows, they rattled enough to make our hearts swell.

"Honey, it's cold out outside," I sang to him. Cold enough that even my words shivered.

People froze to death in these parts. We had put ourselves in a spot where problems wouldn't be resolved before the evening news. Perhaps, when Rob opened our stove door to push another log into the flame, he was eclipsing anything he did all day. So significant was warmth to our family when it was this cold.

I thought of that when he opened the Bible to read to me. I drank in the words. I thought of the songs. Were other Christians sitting close together around a hot stove, singing and crying to God like we were? "More holiness give me."

My dress turned out great. Simple lines with a scroll collar. I cut off the socks to the right length and sewed new feet in them. The Nueuschwander's were ready for church.

ROB

Ready for the message! When we took our places in the pew, we had completed a frenzy of effort that started before dawn. We might admit to having second thoughts as to why we were doing this, when we were untying scarfs and pulling jackets off the girls.

"What in the world are you kids trying to do to yourselves up on that mountain?" people kept asking us.

What seemed a destiny, peculiar for us while we up there doing it, gave us pause when we saw ourselves through the eyes of the more serene and sensible Christians. Funny, when getting ready for church would mean a quick shower, having Sunday clothes hanging - waiting for us, smelling new toast-jam-and coffee; when the biggest Sunday morning crisis was finding our Bibles and Sunday School books, we hadn't gone.

Now, we hardly dared relate what we went through to get ready for church. Folks might have thought we were either bragging or stretching it.

Water: Does anyone believe that it doesn't come bubbling from a faucet? Hot? Isn't that the way God created it? Pulling water from the spring took no more than brute strength. But now, in January, every night, the hole I chopped the day before froze over good and deep during the night. I had to try and break through it with a post, or chop a new hole big enough for a pail, and try to get that pail, which was tied to a pole, up through the hole without spilling it. Then try and get that pail up an icy slope to our cabin. We understood how people could get in bloody fights over water. We understood the murmuring of the Israelites who went three days without it.

We brought water from town for drinking. It was easier than chopping through the frozen over holes. But water brought from town presented a conflict. We had our choice of putting the chains back on Brutus to get up our driveway, or lugging it two miles up a very slippery hill to the house. Many times we opted for chopping the holes, but we found another solution. We discovered that melting snow was a way to get water for washing, and snow we had in abundance.

Every morning, getting out of the house was a challenge. Getting across the yard had to be delayed until the little detail of shoveling made it possible. These wintry details became a process called 'facing a day.' On Sunday morning, the church clock made it a crisis.

We didn't want to be late. The whole encompassing job seemed a commission from God.

Both Becky and I noted that our prayers and Bible study were not unlike the seasons of refreshing we had discovered, years ago, at Bible Camps.

We kept praying, "More Holiness give us." I kept

remembering the verse, "If your earthly father knows how to give you good gifts - how much more your Heavenly Father." I claimed it, for I felt forgiven.

We'd sing on our knees and we reread the 4th chapter of James. "Give us more grace," we'd pray together.

James would answer, 'He giveth grace to the humble.'

"Make us more humble," we'd cry out to God.

'Be afflicted and mourn' ... read the scripture.

'and weep' ... we read in James. 'Humble yourselves in the sight of the Lord and He will lift you up' ...

Should we ask "why" when the ice is thick? When we can't get to town for water and melted snow water tastes strange and hard to swallow? Was winter the abrasive for honing our hearts? Is this how we learn in our Mountain Monastery?

Is there a soul cleansing, a purifying of the spirit, that comes only with trouble? ... we were flooded with remembering the words of testimony from Christians who had felt the hard hand of adversity ... "We drew closer to the Lord," they'd tell us or "We grew in the Lord."

We knew the feeling. We felt a soul warmth and closeness to our Savior that we had never felt before. We even wondered if what the old time revival preachers had was help from the hard hand of adversity to melt the soul and spirit. There was no other way to describe it, but broken, melted and poured out.

Coming from the strange sanctuary on our hill, we were ready for Don's words. The love of Christ was warm and fresh as we prayed together, sang together, and listened to his word.

And then we got goats!

We hadn't planned to get them during these snow-bound days of January, but once again we saw an ad in the paper. For Free! There is no better price.

How could we pass up something like this? Wasn't it what we wanted? Goats? Chickens? Rabbits, too? Tasha had the sniffles so she would stay home with Mama. It was Anja that would be my helper. She giggled and danced as she crawled into her snowsuit and boots.

And she stood tall and close as she assured me, "I'll help you, Daddy." I was so proud of her. To think I had hoped for a boy! I had this beautiful being standing beside me who looked up and assured me that she would be my helper today.

She danced and fell in the snow until she looked like a walking snowball. I tried to break path for her, but she'd have no part of it. She tackled the drifts much like a snowplow. If she stumbled, it was headfirst. I'd hear a little voice and then find where it came from when the mouth broke through. It was fun.

The truck started with no trouble, and we found the farmer with no trouble. The farmer questioned our ability to take care of these pets that they had grown so fond of. Little Anja assured him that they would be loved, every one, because that was what she was trying to do. The farmer seemed to be concerned that these animals get to a good home rather than bring a good price. The stipulations for our getting animals could not have been more in our favor. Anja cinched the deal.

And loading them was easier than a lot of our undertakings. These tame animals were loaded in our truck more by trust of a human hand than any manhandling could have wrought. We were on our way with a handshake. Anja was almost too entranced to even wave good-bye to these good people.

But I vowed that afternoon, that were I a writer, I would send off reams about the madness that can be generated by a bunch of squawking hens.

We loaded our animals carefully on our sled for the ride up the hill to our little paradise. A crate of rabbits and hens in the middle, with a goat walking on each side. It looked like a little paradise to us as we made our way over the bumps and ridges in our path. Anja ran around dividing her love pats among the creatures. And then, of course, it happened. We hit a bump and over went our hen crate, bouncing open one of the doors.

I decided then, that even if I were a writer I could never describe the pandemonium. Those hens flew all directions at once. They knocked off my cap. Decorated all of us, slapdash. Blued the air with hen-swear that the whole world understands. "RUN FOR COVER."

That's what our two goats tried to do. One on each side of me, they split and tangled themselves up with me and Anja completely. They screamed sounds none of us knew that goats could make. We all screamed.

"Becky!! Becky!! Becky!!"

Not a movement from the hill.

"Mama! Mama! Mama!" Anja pleaded to our windows. The goats were climbing her little body and bleating piteously.

"Mama, come!"

Is she deaf? Completely deaf? How could any human not hear all this noise. The hens had taken to the woods still screaming their indignation. That was what got Becky's attention.

Finally she poked her head out the door and came out to watch the commotion in the woods. Wouldn't she even look this way? She did, and then she did the last thing I ever dreamed she'd do.

She laughed.

Uproariously.

But she untangled a little girl from a frightened goat. I got my legs loose and found my goat pushing against me in terror, but I was able to lead them home. We tied them. Gave them the hay the farmer sent with us. The poor little bunnies huddled in the corners of their cage. They would wait until morning to try something as civil as eating. Very soon, I noticed the sweet animal smell in the small room we had partitioned for our livestock. I think both Becky and I felt a kinship to those who had lived before us, who rounded out their lives with these gentle creatures that shared a common bond with mankind. They, too, had been created.

I thought of that when I broke a loaf of Becky's bread and tossed it to the crazy hens that were still cackling in the woods. I no longer wanted to chop off their heads for soup. We coaxed them to the shelter and hoped they would find a roost before morning.

"You know Rob," Becky whispered that night as we were floating off in drowsiness while rehashing another experience of living that we had shared, "of all the things that have happened here, I'll bet we'll laugh about this the most."

Chapter 16

BECKY

Eggs! Now the problem was what to do with them. We couldn't believe that our hens were laying only one egg a day! We could have sworn that Monday they were doing double time. Egg salad sandwiches, potato salad with lots of eggs, fried eggs, boiled eggs, eggs benedict. We did not complain. After our introduction to no food at all, we just ate eggs and praised God. Perhaps our favorite was egg pancakes.

1 cup of flour ... every day I accurately measured it
6 eggs
1/2 cup sugar
2 cups of milk
1 teaspoon of salt
1/2 cup real butter

I'd mix them together. Some days I'd separate the eggs, beat the whites stiff, and fold them in last. Either way they were our sustenance and our dessert. We never tired of them, and any left over were rolled with a sprinkle of sugar and served as a cookie.

And the goats were milking. Goat milk? I knew it was nutritious and could be used for cooking and baking, but drinking it? I was a skeptic. But it was good beyond belief. We only fed and watered the rabbits. Rob hadn't gotten around to getting them ready for rabbit pie. Of our venture with animals, the chickens were our best investment. We bought grain and hay for the rest of them, but the chickens devoured our table scraps and gave us their wonderful eggs in return.

We were asked to sing, but we were not singing, nor was Rob preaching. We didn't feel ready. Our excuse was the roads. Anyone up here could understand that. Snow was bad, but soon we would have mud, and the natives have a way of preparing you for it.

"Wait 'til we get the mud," they'd say. "You haven't seen anything yet."

We both felt church was our top priority. Being there on time did not go unnoticed. When our pew was vacant, the parishioners knew something was wrong, and they were right.

Our Sunday morning skirmish had become more routine. We had packed into our truck, close to each other. We knew our spots well. I felt as good about my curtain dress as perhaps I will ever feel good about any dress in my life. The seams were holding.

The truck had started with little trouble. Rob had learned its ways and knew when a too eager push on the accelerator would flood it.

We were coming down the hill at twenty-five, that was the speed limit. Anja was pointing out the rabbit trails and Tasha, not to be outdone, was pointing to a chickadee. I tried to catch both observations; it made our family dynamics work better. Rob was trying to match the family enthusiasm about the new snow that had trails in it and chickadees too. Suddenly the truck lurched.

"Oh God!" Rob screamed. "Oh God, help us!"

"Honey," I screamed back. "Turn! Turn! You're heading off the mountain, Rob! Turn! Turn! Turn!"

The truck was crashing through the underbrush out of control! Tipping! Bouncing! Throwing us against the windshield. We were falling against Rob. Despite my strength to hold to the dashboard, I was falling against the girls. I tried to shield their faces from the windshield and pressed their heads to my heart.

There was nothing we could do. We were in God's hands. The brush was coming at us as though we were facing boulders. I could see the drop off. It looked like a precipice, and we were tearing up the earth as we lunged toward it. As the front tipped forward, the back of the truck bounced up - we were going to roll.

"Oh God!" I cried. "We are dying - dying." I could almost see my mother waiting. I knew how badly I needed her. "Jesus, we're coming," I called.

I saw Rob's face. It was white - with no color. "I can't turn - Becky - the steering rod broke!"

The cab was rolling, we were going - going - and suddenly the thought of dying together seemed sweet. The thought of living after a crash like this was what seemed scary. How would we ever get out? Would anybody ever find us? Would we bleed to death? I somehow relaxed and waited for the will of God.

Finally, the convulsing, heaving truck collided. The pine tree did not break or bend. It stopped us. There was dead silence.

No one spoke. I wondered if we were dead. No one moved. Is this the way it feels to come to after those terrible wrecks we read about?

"Rob," I whispered, "We're crushing the children. We've got to get out of here."

"I know Becky — I know! Oh - dear - God - help - me! It's OK Babies, Daddy will get you out of here!"

He was buried by us on top of him. We were all a tangle of arms and legs. The youngsters started to whimper, but when he solaced them, they waited. They felt secure in the arms of their father.

He squirmed, he wiggled in his struggle. He pulled on the steering wheel to get leverage, and with his other hand he reached behind the seat and pulled himself out. He had freed himself.

He stood on the steering column and reached for the door handle. It unlatched easily, but the door was too heavy to lift. He rolled down the window and heaved himself through it. He had made it.

"The girls!" His voice had grown hoarse with the struggle. "Lift Anja to me, Becky." I struggled to get my feet on something solid. I pulled at Anja who was wiggling to untangle herself. She didn't cry. She knew what she had to do. Her Daddy was kneeling on the door and reaching for her through the window. She was able to grab his hand. I gave her a boost, and she made it through the window.

Together we got Tasha out, and now it was my turn. It wasn't easy, but I crawled out with Rob pulling me. It was then I realized - we might have bruises, but we had no broken bones and no one was bleeding.

Rob looked over the canyon precipice. "Oh Becky. Oh God!" It was all he could say. We breathed our gratitude to our Lord, but Rob was confused.

"This is insane! Is that what you are telling me,

God? That it's insane to do what we are trying to do?"

I don't have money to fix my trucks! They break in two. The steering rod breaks so we start rolling down the canyon! That truck could have blown up! God, what are you trying to tell me?" He was screaming to the universe.

"I have to give up!" He was shouting nonstop. "We got to go back so I can get a decent job, Becky, and support my family. Oh God, what does Paul say about the man who does not provide for his family? Is this providing? - to have my family dangling over a canyon? I got to give up! I got to go back!" he told God.

I had an experience I could draw on. I knew how it felt to think that everything was over. That there would be no more problems because Rob had closed out on life. I remembered standing in the parlor in Spokane and screaming my thanks to God that we still had problems. That he was alive. That the strap had broken and all we had troubling us now was problems. And they were dwarfed because the man I loved was alive!

"Are we like the Israelites?" I asked Rob. "After they had been led through the Red Sea, they murmured because they had no leeks, no onions, and wanted to turn back." I looked back at Old Brutus. He looked so pathetic. I did wonder how we ever got out.

We were alive! We had feet we could walk on! We had feet we could dance on! We could sing!

"Rob honey! Look at me! At Anja! At Tasha! We are alive! Give us a hug! Let's dance! Let's sing! Come skip with me."

We put our arms around each other and skipped and sang. "Thank God from whom all blessings flow." At the top of our lungs we sang it. No one could hear us shouting to God on our mountain. We almost wished they could - we wanted the world to hear it.

ROB

They missed us at church, and they came looking. Everyone was concerned about the icy slopes that stood between us and where we wanted to go out here. They knew that no one had better slopes than we did. When we weren't there, our minister asked Charles and Rick of our worship team to go looking for us. They knew something was wrong.

They caught us skipping and singing. Becky would always amaze me! How can she come through singing after we were sliding toward a drop off. They found us euphoric and praising the Lord.

I told them how I had felt 'That's it!' - 'We had tried and it didn't work.' - 'I was a failure!' - I wasn't supporting my family!' Becky told them she thought this was where the Lord wanted us, and we shouldn't ever think of giving up - ! They agreed with Becky. But there was that detail of getting the truck out of the woods.

Becky put on the coffee pot and served some of her egg creations while we figured out how we were going pull this off.

"Do you know that farmer down the hill from you, Rob? He seems to have a pretty good truck," Charles said as he reached for one of Becky's rolled pancakes.

"Oh boy, do I know him. Charles. Good ole Brad." My neck itched and my forehead itched, seemed all I could do was squirm and rub where it itched. "I helped him hay last summer, and he's been telling me I wouldn't last here six months. 'The most I'll give you is a year,' he said the last time he pulled me out."

"You mean he's pulled you out before?" Rick seemed amused.

"Yeah, at least a couple times. I even had to borrow money from him once when I was working for him. Wow! I sure feel like a loser. This is going to be hard on my pride."

"I can understand that! But a man has to do what a man has to do, and you got to get that truck out of there." Rick stirred his coffee more than necessary. I knew he was feeling genuinely sorry for me.

"I know." I was stirring my coffee too. "One thing I should have going for me is a good dose of humility after all this. Wonder if you can take pride in that."

We finished our coffee. "No time like the present!" I had begun to wonder who coined those good sayings, and wondered if I'd ever leave a saying that some poor fish might quote when he was in a fix.

Brad was in good spirits. I guess my situation was so bad that he didn't think it warranted any ribbing. Besides, he was a good person and seemed to respect me for sticking to it. Didn't say as much - but I knew he felt it.

When we found the truck, we realized how close we came to toppling over the cliff. We had slid around a couple trees and rammed into the two trees that stood between us and the bottom of the canyon.

"We'll have to get rid of those pines behind you, there, if we're going to get this rig out," Brad advised. We cut the trees and ran a cable through the block and tackle on Brad's truck. When the truck pulled, old Brutus backed up the slope with no complaints.

Now all we had to do was fix it. "If you go to the wrecking yard in town, you should find parts," Brad said.

Something like a hospital, the wrecking yard kept the moving parts moving in this part of the country. They knew the makes, the year and the name of every mechanical part of almost any machine. I would need a steering wheel column.

Nothing empties the checkbook like instant adversity. When I wrote the check for the parts, it was almost gone. But we had weathered the worst of the winter. All I had to do now was become a wilderness mechanic like most of the survivors in these hills. When Brutus was able to move again, I'd have to get back in the woods. Steven County had one of the highest unemployment rates.

Keeping our spirits up was the example we found in Dan Stone and his wife, the youth pastor of our little church. They seemed to be starving in the ministry too, and he had to do outside work to support his family. Young - they were both about our age. He was blonde, tall, good looking with large glasses. The one thing that impressed us was their faithfulness to the Lord.

Their struggle in meeting the necessities of life made both of them a walking epistle of what Becky and I wanted to be. When we joined them in the after service, we knew they just weren't kidding. This was no high performance act. He had given up the opportunity to take over his Dad's wheat ranch to serve the Lord full time.

They praised God as though they hardly noticed the struggle. We wanted that, Becky and I. A spirit of praise without fear of the struggle.

About this time I ran into Zane. A mystery man of sorts. One you never forget and find remembering sort of painful. He had no problems with self doubt. He pegged people, each fit into a category of his blunt appraisal. His reckoning - he drew from life experience.

He would teach me how to cut and deliver to town nine cords of wood in one day. He thought it was his destiny to do that, and one day we did it. The average was six cords in one day.

"Hear ya aim to cut some wood this spring." We were standing in the church entry before tackling the outside elements.

"Yes Zane!" I rose to the opportunity of making some money.

"Had any experience? Are you a woodsman? A logging woodsman?" He revved back and rammed his hands in his mackinaw to give me a head to foot appraisal. I thought my hands were showing the effects of winter in these parts, but compared to Zane's knotty knuckles, split nails and calluses, they must have looked pretty soft.

"I'm a hard worker Zane."

"Wal, it's like this. We could cut wood from the slash piles left by the loggers in the National forest. You know where Chewelah Creek is?"

"Think I've heard of it."

"Wal, it's at the North Fork of Chewelah Creek." Zane only had one tone of voice - rough and loud. "It's really a two man job. I have a block and tackle set up in my truck, and we just hook the chain around a bunch of logs and pull them out of the pile with the truck."

"Great!" I enthused. "Like I said, Zane, I'm not afraid of hard work!" It seemed he was looking at my hands, so I rammed them in my pockets too.

"OK. Meet you at the park tomorrow morning at five."

"Did you say five, Zane?"

"Yep." He took off with the determined gait of one who made resolute decisions that worked.

He would toughen me.

"Wow!" Becky said as we pulled for home.

I hardly slept all night. Afraid of how I'd be if I didn't get any sleep. Afraid of how I'd be if I overslept or couldn't handle this thing. I knew the balance in my checkbook.

Spring break-up was over. This was the mud season. A new experience in the woods. Our Bible reading was short. Our prayers were short. We were trying to balance our spiritual quest with earning a living. For now, with those two goals, all else was inconsequential.

I made it. Zane was there with his truck and his huge Percheron horse.

"Great horse. Ain't nothin' this horse can't pull. Look at all that dead timber in them ravines. Never could git the blame things out without Smokey here. Ya can go down and hook a chain on any of them logs and Ole Smokey will pull it right up."

He wanted to give me a demonstration. I waded through the underbrush down the side of the ravine and hooked the chain around a fallen tree.

"Gee!" he hollered as he gave old Smokey a slap on the rear. "Gee!"

The horse seemed to unravel his massive muscles, you could see them bulge as power surged through and they prepared to pull. He lowered his head. He pulled and the tree moved right up the mountainside. Zane gave Smokey a slap on the shoulder and scratched his ears with affection. "Good job, old Boy," he said. This man knew his trucks, his timber and his Percheron.

But his time schedule and mine never quite fused. When I was tussling to get the chain released from the log, Zane would appraise my efforts.

"My Grandmother could unhook that log quicker'n that!"

We were here to do business with the slash lumber and to prove what we could get done in one day. The misery in getting it done was par for the day. When I reached overhead to hook the chain around the slash wood, a loose end had my cap on it with a hank of hair."

"That ought to wake ya up!" Zane shouted his sympathy.

Seemed that Zane was always waiting for me - gunning his motor.

"Anytime now!" Zane hollered over his shoulder.

Zane revved his truck and started to pull. The towering pile let go of its chained lumber, but not without complaint. As the truck dug in and moved, the chained bundle crashed to the ground.

When a stray piece slammed into my shin Zane yelled, "Watch it, Bozo! Do I have to tell you everything?"

We would now cut it to stove length size and pile it in the trucks for delivery. I took this assignment like the challenge of my life. I worked up a sweat trying to keep up, but Zane was always at least two logs ahead.

"You'll never make a logger at that rate!" Zane tossed me his encouragements.

I discovered something about working fast together. Two men who synchronize their efforts can do the work of three.

Everyday I learned more about Zane. He was never socially verbal. But in bits and pieces, when we stood by the warming fire, I learned something about this intense man. He had found the Lord in prison. His heart and intent was good. His manner was crusty and his exterior was, pure and simple, just Zane.

He had trouble with my Becky. "How'd ya handle a woman like that? Pretty fancy, I'd say. How can she work with those long fingernails?"

We did cut and deliver nine cords of wood in one day. Zane split the profits fifty-fifty. He was a person who kept his word. And honesty was just one of the virtues of this solid man.

He would pit his determination to support his wife against adversity. We cut logs four feet across and split them like cutting pie wedges. By some freak twist of the knee, he fell and tore the ligaments of his leg.

I splinted his leg and got him to the doctor who told him he would have to be off his feet for a couple of months at least.

Only then did I see old Zane cry. "How can I support my wife?" His voice broke.

The church men gathered to pray for him and anoint his leg with oil like the scripture commanded.

Zane was back in the woods in a week, limping and working. We were bound by what we had in common. Two men that had to put food on the table.

BECKY

Zane was rubbing off on both of us. His cutting to the bone of what was essential to get things done was his hallmark of how you do it.

No wasted words. No wasted fluff in his world. Money for the essentials was the job to be done, and Rob was falling in step. The mud of March and April made the steps slippery, but in Zane's world of no excuses, you figured out how to get where you were going. I had some trouble with that.

And this was the time that Rob got hooked on the value of chickens. Spring seemed to mean chickens, chickens, chickens, to Rob. It did me too, but it also meant flowers and a bit of green grass around our cabin.

I had spent a week with my sister Vicky in Spokane. We both were at our creative best. I had forgotten that there was a world where people simply walked over to a table, picked up a menu, and actually the biggest decision of the day was what tickles your fancy. Dressing?

White or dark bread? Rice or baked potato?

My sister was relieved that Rob and I seemed to be working things out, but she still thought we were 'out to lunch,' and that's the expression she used.

"Becky! Aren't you wasting your talents spending all your hours up there just surviving? Hard to figure out just where it's getting you."

"Well Vicky, we're trying to live on faith."

"Honey, we have churches here, packed three times a day, with people trying to do the same thing." That was a thought. I'd witnessed the earnest Christians praying for faith in God's way for their lives, and they were not starving and rolling down a mountain cliff trying to find it.

Her pretty home with matched linen and a wardrobe that smelled of cologne made a mountain cabin quite a stark contrast. Especially when I remembered the moat of mud I'd have to wade through to reach it.

Especially when you come home and find a large crate filled with chickering noises, waiting for you in the driveway.

"Rob, whatever have you done now!" That was my greeting to my husband I hadn't seen in a week.

"Well Becky, they had a sale on these Rhode Island Red chicks."

"Rob, how many are there?"

"A hundred - they only sell them by the hundred."

A hundred! It may as well have been locusts sweeping down on us. To this city girl, he just plain didn't know what he was doing.

What are your planning to do with them?

"Feed them. Water them. Watch them grow into big fat roosters and hens. We'll butcher the roosters and fill a locker with good chicken meat. The hens will lay those big brown eggs that you can sell for a little money in your pocketbook."

"Come on, let's skip and sing —" he continued eagerly. "Come and see! Come and see! Let's skip. It's great to have you home again!"

My feet couldn't leave the ground. "Where are you going to keep them, Rob?"

"They don't take much space while they're little. I'll hang a lightbulb in the shed, and they'll huddle around it. Look! I even ordered the chicken feed!"

"Rob, I wanted just a little money for flowers and grass seed!"

"Who said you can't have it?"

They ate and grew like chickens do. Big. At first, old grocery bags, newspaper, any kind of wrapping paper became their floor covering, but as soon as the sun warmed the earth so my grass seeds began to sprout, that was where they wandered. Not only did they eat every little sprout, they squatted and scratched the dirt and seeds up through their feathers, ducked their heads and scratched the dirt over them. They were bent on putting an end to my spot of grass. But they were also bent on doing the same to the purple petunias I had planted.

For weeks, I had not seen my cabin centered in a moat of mud. I had envisioned a green lawn with flowers cascading over the edges surrounding it. This was not wrong. God gave us dominion over His earth. Shouldn't I make our part of it beautiful to enhance His handiwork? The chickens sure made short work of that dream.

And the goats helped. There was foliage in the woods for them, but they relished everything we planted better. Rob planted a garden, and the goats finished it off.

I was angry. I prayed for a peaceful spirit, and I

stormed at Rob.

"You get these animals and we have no fences. They are taking over our spot here, while we just exist in the mud."

"Becky! I know how you feel, but I don't have time to fence or money to buy the fencing!"

"Then why do you bring home all these animals?" I screamed.

"So they can grow while I'm earning the money. Can't you understand that?"

I couldn't. He was still putting in unreasonable hours with Zane. Both he and Zane were working fervently and often tempestuously to store up firewood for the coming winter. Rob had covered about a quarter acre with it.

The irony was that Rob and Zane could look at their mountain of wood with a hand-rubbing feel of satisfaction. I looked at my efforts with frustration, tears and anger. At the chickens and goats that I now hated, at Rob who seemed the cause of it, and even at God who wouldn't help me overcome. What I wanted was instant victory!

Much of the time I was just plain mad. And even that was better than the depression I couldn't shake.

It would bother me to hear women tell of the obstacles in their lives and the wonderful victory they had. The worse their predicaments the more they overcame. It actually sounded like bragging to me because it wasn't that way for me. Did they ever have goats and chickens on their doorsteps so that every time their kids came in they had to kick off their shoes to leave the manure outside?

When the goats finished off my petunias, Rob really felt sorry for me. He surprised me with a huge basket of hanging flowers. It cost over twelve dollars.

"Honey, I know how hard you try to make this place beautiful. He hung them outside the window where I could see them when coming in or going out. They cascaded down in blooms and ivy. They were lovely.

For two days!

I had met Rob so we could walk in together. Supper was waiting, and I wanted to show him how grateful I was for the flowers. I pointed to them and we both gasped - Nubbins had scaled the roof, slid down to get both knees in the pot, and looked at us with her mouth full of my purple petunias. Laugh or cry? That paradox has plagued God's mankind, I supposed, through every generation. Now we had to deal with it.

I cried. We both knew how hard the other guy was trying. We just held to each other as Rob wiped the tears from my cheeks.

But was there no overcoming for me? It wasn't the New Year's Eve incident anymore. It was the here and now where I needed the victory. I needed to totally overcome my need for a cigarette. Totally overcome my need to holler at Rob. My feelings of being gypped because of the way I lost my mother.

Rob was patient, but it got to him. Once when I was hollering at him he banged out of the door.

"Where do you think you're going?" I demanded as I ran to holler after him.

"I'm heading for the roof!" he shot back. That cooled me off and sent me to my knees. "It's better to dwell on the roof than in a house with a nagging woman." We had just read the scripture.

I prayed and I prayed. "God, is there no victory for me?"

ROB

It wasn't that we didn't have a game plan. We did and it flavored our mealtime, followed our Bible reading, sprinkled through our prayers. We even took it to bed with us. We had to raise $2,500.00 to buy those Alpines from our Montana friends for our Christmas tree sales. I had placed the order.

Now it was June, and we had to add a new and terrible word to our mountain vocabulary. We couldn't decide on its origin or its connection, we only learned what it meant. **HOOT OWL meant Fire Danger — Stay out of the woods.**

And we also learned that when there is no rain from the skies that water dries up everywhere. The spring dried up. The well dried up. The pond dried up. Mud turns to dirt that blows in the hot wind and covers everyone and everything inches deep. And everyone is thirsty.

1985 was the driest year on record in our parts. The goats, the chickens, Becky, the girls and I seemed to be thirsty all the time. I couldn't get in the woods, so our game plan was put on hold while we waited for a soaking rain.

My responsibilities took on a new twist. I had to keep water in my compound. Every living thing drinks water.

It was hot. Sticky hot. The chickens gasped their breathing efforts. The goats panted. The girls got prickly heat and cried. And I was stumbling hot. With my plans for Christmas sales on hold, I felt as though I was stumbling along an unmarked path.

Every day seemed to arrive with a — 'now what?'

destiny. I wasn't praying for miracles as much as I was praying for strength for the day. Others had coped with drought. How did they do it? If they left their efforts on written record, I had never read them. None but Habakkuk, who became my study guide during these days of no rain. "Although the fig tree shall not blossom, neither fruit be on the vines — yet I will rejoice in my Lord, I will joy in the God of my salvation." Someone had marked my path for me. "The Lord God is my strength," he wrote. "He will make my feet like the feet of a deer."

I bought a water pump. It worked until the spring ran completely dry. We had to save water to prime the suction plunger, but when the spring ran completely dry, nothing came through the water spout.

"The Lord is my strength." I'd heard it in testimony and sang it, more concerned about the harmony than the message of those words. Now I actually cried the words. "If it worked for Habakkuk, make it work for me, Lord. If I can't leap like a deer, help my stumbling feet. My family needs water."

I hauled water from the Chewelah City Park in five gallon jugs. One day I drove in the yard to meet my thirst crazed family only to find that the jugs had rolled off the back of the truck. We all cried together. I had to make a return trip and look for them. I found them - one had broken. Every other need was deferred. Water now was more important than food. I thanked God that we at least had air. What was vital for survival was my job to fend for.

I didn't pray to be spared. I prayed for a way.

I just wished I wasn't such a greenhorn. I caught myself wondering how Zane handled this. As trying as it was to do, I did ask him.

"How does a man make a living in times like this, Zane?"

Using these Hoot Owl days wisely came quickly to him. He had the cunning to cope with mountain ways. "Why, we'll jest pack that timber we've been piling in our Wood Bank on your acre over yonder. We'll pack it into town and collect some of our money."

We packed our trucks and made our deliveries. Old Brutus was working almost as good as ever and Zane's ankle was just about as good as ever.

I had never heard Zane sing, but I would now. He attacked his singing like he did almost everything else. With great and singular gusto.

"Now we can fellowship." He often mentioned getting his "second wind.' He did that with a long, deep breath as we unflexed our muscles after loading all that wood for our ride into town. Zane was ready to sing.

"Praise the name of Je - sus," he sang with all the voice God gave him.

"Praise the name of Je - sus

"We have the vic - tor - y"

It wasn't George Beverly Shae. It was Zane and me. And no one could have meant it more.

There's something about muscling into the adventure of wrestling a living out of the timber that grows around you that is splendid. About bringing water home so those in one's care could drink their fill. I wondered if this would be part of life that I would look back on with longing. For the feeling of standing between my family and the elements was akin to something as noble as anything I had known.

The Adventist School bought sixty cords of our wood, which helped our tree fund. While we were selling our wood during Hoot Owl time, we were praying for rain. And it did rain.

The sky did not brood a while and then start with a slow warning sprinkle as it did closer to the coast. The sky would blast its thunder, open up and pour. The drops bombarded the dust, and the dust exploded around them. And surprisingly, the dry hard dust did not open up to receive them. It seemed to close ranks so the water poured off in sheets and ran in torrents down any kind of slope. Pools formed all over. We danced in them. The animals contorted their heads and stretched up into the rain. The goats chased each other. The birds sang. We joined them. We were crazy with the joy of rain. We praised God.

The scent of new rain is like no other. We would have liked to bottle it. The earth comes forth with a fragrance that spells promise of new life. New sprouts on the willow. Wilted rows in the garden raise their heads. We stood soaked, with arms upraised in the warm rain, and blended our voices to our Lord. "Will we ever sing like this again?" we asked each other. We had almost forgotten how well we could sing together.

"Sing Anja! Sing Tasha! Sing to God!" Up on this mountain our little family joined together to sing and sing our praises. We almost felt sorry for folks who would never share our moment. It rained for days.

We had chosen a spot of extremes. The most frigid of winters. Hot and dry summers. Perhaps it took the elements at their rawest to teach these seekers what God wants from His people. Christians with character who trust God regardless of circumstance. Christians who had discovered that as your day - so shall your strength be ...

But God was not through with us yet. Whoever coined the thought - it must have been meant for us.

BECKY

There was Tamarack up on Calispel Mountain, and I was hearing from Rob during every waking hour that we could get $110.00 a cord for Tamarack. We still didn't have enough money for the trees.

I decided I must help. I wasn't a city girl any longer. I was the wife of a man who was trying to learn the ways of God. I recognized a bulldog tenacity in my husband when he set about with a purpose in mind. I had thought his ugly-tree idea was totally crazy from day one last year, and he proved me wrong. It was time I get in the woods to help.

Anja would be starting school in September, but we had a month together where she could help entertain Tasha while I helped Rob load the trucks. It made our mornings take on the dash of a Chicago train depot with me calling off the stations.

"If you get the water in the boiler I can wash out some clothes when we get back."

"Anja. Try and roll up the quilts so Daddy can pile

them in the back of the truck."

"Anja, bring your picture books and blocks so you can play with Tasha on the blankets."

"Rob, do you remember where we put the mosquito repellent?"

I packed a lunch with plenty of egg pancakes. Milk in thermos for the girls, and coffee in thermos for us. I didn't forget to be grateful for the inventions I had taken for granted all my life. The pioneers didn't have thermos bottles or mosquito repellent. I had learned such a healthy respect for those wonderful people that I found myself picking up anything they left behind them that I could find. They stood as a testimonial as to how those great people survived, and I wanted my home to forever enshrine them. I felt close to those pioneer mothers as I packed my youngsters off for the woods in the morning.

I really was eager to help, but it was the Old Willys pick-up that gave me the willies. Rob had bought it because it was such a powerful little thing. Someone had put a powerful 327 engine into the tiny little Willys. It felt like the engine would take off and leave me sitting with my load. I hadn't gotten over what a mountain trail did to Old Brutus last winter.

Rob had cut and split the wood, and now he would toss it in the trucks and I would pile up the loads. He drove Brutus and I drove the Willys. Even though Brutus had almost busted in two last winter, I felt safer to have the children ride with him.

Up on Calispel Mountain we all learned a deep and healthy respect for each other. I could hardly believe the tireless energy of my husband, and he kept telling me he couldn't believe his wife, with her long fingernails, could make such a good lumberjack. We both were awed by the unselfish efforts of Anja to entertain her little sister. And little Tasha scratched her mosquito bites and laughed when her blocks fell over because the ground was uneven. We loved each other and hugged each other often. There was a bonding in this mountain enterprise.

Except when I had to lead our caravan around the curves that dipped into drop-offs on the way home. Every touch on the accelerator made the little Willys jump ahead, and I could feel the load trying to catch up behind. And then Old Brutus pulled up right behind me; he was taking the curve too. I prayed for my brakes and I prayed for his. Surviving one curve only led to a worse one. I could feel the streams of sweat running down my back ... There was more than one reason why I wanted the children to ride with Rob. I smoked non-stop. My cigarettes didn't help my nervousness, but trying to not smoke enhanced it.

"Game for another try at it tomorrow?" Rob was so proud of me he was beaming.

"Why of course, honey." It wasn't exactly a lie. I would do it, but I wasn't sure I was all that game about it.

That was how we raised the rest of the money for the trees and how we got $400.00 for Emily, our beautiful jersey cow.

ROB

"Rob honey, whenever you spend that much time with the want ads I wonder what is going to happen next." Becky's face was next to mine as she leaned over my shoulder, trying to spot the ad that was getting my attention. I noticed that her hair hung in curls over her shoulder, she smelled of cologne and her fingernails were getting in shape again.

This was becoming a beautiful winter. We had money in the bank again - six thousand dollars of it. The Christmas tree sales were a smash hit. We had learned from last year to avoid some of the calamities like setting the tent on fire.

We had learned to work together to embellish a project rather than dismantle it. Becky caught the spirit this year and was on the lot with the girls to help me. We had bought an old travel trailer and brought it on the lot, so our project was not unlike a camp out. Becky confessed to liking the feel of the dollar bills almost as much as I did. We had learned how to work together on the lot, and we also had a great Christmas.

Now it was snowing outside, and we just let it pile up. I knew what paths had to be shoveled in the morning. Becky knew how much snow had to be melted for the day. It had become part of our morning routine. We had all the soft snow water we could use.

She also had learned how to get her clothes dry in mountain winters and felt she had outsmarted the elements. She would toss them over the line and when they were frozen, she'd bring them in to dry behind the heater. The sweet aroma of drying clothes made the room moist and fresh. Pulling up to the heat where all this was happening made winter a comfortable friend to have around.

Anja had started school and was proud of her two mile trek down our driveway to the school bus. I kept the path clear for her by driving Brutus with his massive chains forth and back. One trip compacted the snow into a chain-decorated, hard-packed walkway for her.

Becky's happy chatter with the children made the

place homelike by just being in it. And she had done a lot of decorating. She had given our old refrigerator what she called a sponge paint treatment, so it matched the big ruffled blue pricillas that hung crisp on her clean kitchen windows.

And we were back studying our Bible and praying. People kept telling us that we should use our talents for the Lord, but neither of us felt ready. Right now, we would settle for holiness and power. "Power in prayer," we would sing on our knees, "and power with Thee."

There was a problem. Fresh milk. The goats had quit milking and we were used to our daily supply right here in our compound. Taking Brutus down the two mile stretch to the highway and then taking off the chains for the trips to Chewelah to get a gallon of milk and then putting the chains back on to get up our driveway, made a milk supply a vital necessity. After the good goat milk, powdered milk would not do. What we needed now was a cow.

And that was what the ad was all about. A jersey cow for $400.00.

The farmer told me she was ornery. He showed me her milk record, which was superb.

"But why are you selling this good cow? She's beautiful. She's a picture book cow!"

"Because she's ornery. She has her own ideas and doesn't go with the herd, and when she takes off, she takes others with her. I think she'd do OK by herself."

We waited for our new cow. I had fixed a place for her. Moved the livestock around so she would have a spot by herself.

"Emily. Even her name is beautiful, Rob." Becky was giving this new project of mine her try at enthusiasm.

The snow had piled up two feet during the night. I drove Brutus down to the highway and waited for the truck driver to bring Emily. When he arrived, he sized up the snow and the two mile drive up to our place and just plain said he could not make it with his truck.

"Listen," he said convincingly, "she's trail broke. Here, take this switch and she'll just follow in that truck path right up to your barn."

"You really think so?" I was anxious to believe him. I wanted the cow, and I could see that this man was not going to tackle our drive.

"Ya, it won't be a problem. Do you think she'd want to take off in all that snow?"

He convinced me. I paid him the $400.00, and Emily was my cow.

She was beautiful. She looked at me with those soft brown eyes and started up the path with no problem. For fifty feet.

Then she bolted. Took off leaping through the snowdrifts like it had been her way of life. She had just freshened, so her udder was heavy with milk as it bounced over the snowdrifts. At 20 degrees out, I shuddered to think of what it might do to her. Would she ever be able to be milked again?

I ran up to the house. "Honey, please help me. I'm in bad trouble."

"We should be used to that," said my wife as she pulled on her boots.

Becky saw Emily watching us, gasping for air, as she decided what her next move should be.

"Rob honey, she's beautiful. Look at those big black eyes. She's a beauty, Rob! She looks like a big fat deer," Becky cried.

"Do you know how to milk a cow, Rob?"

"No, but I can surely learn. Seems that people the world over have learned how to milk a cow."

"Well, get your little black book, Rob. If you can read it, you can do it. I have faith in you."

"Nice, nice Emily," Becky soothed as we closed in on her. The cow went ahead like she was charmed, and once again I marveled at my wife.

Until we got to the gate of our corral. Emily lived up to her reputation. She whipped around and dashed into the woods and disappeared.

I chased her for what seemed hours. I was falling over undergrowth because I couldn't see. What I needed was a lantern to find her tracks. I held it high, and I held it to the snow which was a foot and a half deep. But her tracks covered her tracks. It was impossible to tell which were the last ones made and if she was heading up the mountain or down,

I followed after her way into the night. I was cold and all I could think of was, my beautiful cow with that full udder is running through the woods destroying herself.

I had to get better boots. When I opened our cabin door, my shoes were so icy I fell to the floor.

"I'm trying, God. I'm trying. What are You trying to do to me? Is it wrong to get a cow so my children can get good milk? Oh God, we almost had her in the shed - literally we did. Help me, help me, God!" I screamed. Somehow each crisis seems the worst when you're going through it.

I followed her trail as it criss-crossed through the mountain. Daylight came and I was still walking, stalking, stumbling, after the marks she left me. All things worked to keep me humble. Her trail led right down to my neighbor below me. The one who pulled me out of the ditch, out of the woods. The one who named me Greenhorn. Now he had my cow tied in a station. She was warm and eating good.

"What have you been up to now?" he asked me mercilessly. What's this cow doing down here?"

I told him I had just bought her, and we almost had her in the corral and all the things that happened to get me in this fix. He'd heard my stories before.

"Do you know how to milk her?" he asked matter-of-factly.

"Well it's no big deal is it? Seems everybody in the world knows how to milk a cow."

"Well there's a trick to it or you can end up with her foot in your bucket."

He showed me what side of the cow you sat on, how to get the milk started, how to strip her so you get all the milk she had. Twice a day I walked down to milk her and brought her rich wonderful milk home. She was a good milker.

"A good cow," Brad told me.

After it stopped snowing, Brad cleared my road off with his four wheel drive and helped me get my cow home. I was glad I had money in the bank to pay him the little I could make him take.

This is the cow we would learn to love. Who would come when I called. When she'd spot me standing outside, she would walk up behind me, slip her head under my arm as though she had that special privilege. She did. I learned to love her like I had loved no other animal.

BECKY

Emily completed the secure, tranquil, sense of snugness we felt this winter on our mountain sanctuary. Our cabin and our little compound had finally become that, a sanctuary. We felt a part of something like a Robinson Crusoe adventure and were doing it in our own style.

Our new cow set the tempo for a morning routine that required gusto. No yawning our way out of bed here. There were no blurry eyes in our household. A cup of coffee was not to wake us up, maybe more like warm us up for the blast of cold when we opened the door. Here, it was cold outside. Often hitting zero, and it was dark - day would come much later ... We didn't slide into the day. Both Rob and I charged into it. The self-starter was 'chores'.

Emily had to be fed, stall cleaned with fresh straw, and her udder had to be washed with warm water. She had to be milked. But before that, Rob fed and watered the goats and the chickens. He also cleaned their stalls. And we had gotten a couple of runty pigs that were waiting for Emily's fresh milk. We all were waiting for her milk.

Her milk was rich. We'd pour it in a pan and push it in the refrigerator so the next morning I could skim off the thickest, richest cream I had ever seen. We'd sour it by leaving it out for a day and then put it in a quart jar and shake it until we watched tiny white lumps forming. The excitement of those tiny lumps becoming a ball of yellow butter never got old.

"Save the buttermilk," Rob would remind me. He'd never drunk buttermilk before.

"Biscuits about ready?" he'd holler at me as he brought a blast of mountain winter morning in with him. The contrast of the hot heater clime with frosted cheeks and fingers always gave him a quick shiver as he hung his mackinaw on the same peg every day and his cap on the other. The little routines that we were developing delighted me.

"Whew! It's great to be in," he'd say and rub his hands. Sometimes he blew on them or run a cold knuckle under my chin.

I had often heard of women 'bustling' and I had just that feel as I flew between the scrambled eggs on the burner and the biscuits in the oven. The girls got up for breakfast. I pulled Tasha's high chair up next to Rob. Anja sat up to the table to eat. Dawdling was not her style. She would be starting her two mile stint down our driveway to the school bus. She fell into the pattern of our place. No fuss. She just did what was expected of her. Often she asked the blessing, thought everything she ate was good, and then came to have her face bundled in a scarf with only her eyes peeking through. If there had been a lot of snow, taking Brutus down the drive as a path-breaker would have been part of Robs pre-breakfast 'chores'.

It was very good. We each enhanced each other's morning. Our mid-winter groove hadn't changed. Rob carried in the water, the wood, I tackled the dishes, made the beds, and swept the floors. We paced each other because we followed last year's pattern for our Bible reading and prayer. We had more time this year. Even with our animals we had the benefit of a tested routine.

Rob had paid the mortgage six months in advance again. Brutus needed a thousand dollars in repairs. We again bought six month's worth of groceries. We got a bed, a washing machine with a wringer. I had grown up with a push-button automatic but this beat the scrub board. And we had a few dollars for decorating.

For one dollar, I got a pail full of odds and ends of wallpaper. I turned our walls into a crazy-quilt design. Perhaps I'll never find a wall design that will rate me such warm compliments from everybody. Rob began encouraging my interest in keeping the decor of our home a place where the efforts of people coping with adversities could be honored. Bread pans and butter molds added warmth and beauty to our home. Their long handled fry pans brought their own kind of charm. Always, there was a reason for a different type of design. Some brought their stories with them.

Rob began building, and each project turned a spot that had frustrated our hours into something that improved our day. He leveled our house and added a porch. He used Randy's leftover scraps of hardwood flooring to lay down a hardwood floor in our kitchen area and leftover carpeting to lay a beautiful brown carpet in our living room. Perhaps nothing delighted me like the cabinets that he and his Dad built into my kitchen. We appreciated each other's efforts and our cabin became our delight ... and it seemed to delight our visitors. People were coming to see us.

Connie, Zane's wife, and I had become friends. There was a bond between two women of mountain men. Perhaps our bond was a gratefulness for a day that they brought no disaster home with them from the hills. Next month Rob would be working for Pernsteiner's Logging. He credited Zane for giving him a crash course in endurance. A mountain man's credo for his kind of job.

Rob had fenced. Next summer, he promised - I would have green grass and a flower garden. Things had gotten very good.

What bothered me most was ... my happiness frightened me. I was suffering from what I called a 'what next?' syndrome. And I couldn't find the strength to kick it or my nicotine demands. I was much better, but I lacked the something to kick the habit.

Mostly, I was troubled by a word in scripture. Someone had put it to song so the word ran through my head continually. I could not shake it - not that I wanted to, but I wanted reprieve from its troubling presence. As we studied the Bible, it hopped out at me, page after page and verse after verse. It was the word *praise*. There was a refrain of the song that I could not escape: *"His praise shall continually be on my lips."* It reminded me that that wasn't the way it was. I was troubled about a lot of things that wiped away my praise.

It seemed that Rob found a continual praise easier than I did, now that he was growing daily with the Lord.

I often heard him in his prayers praising the Lord with words that I didn't understand.

Could that be *talking in tongues*? My upbringing did not deal kindly with the experience: 'it was not for today' and it was something we did not discuss.

Folks continued to ask us to sing. A friend mentioned us to a pastor of a tiny Pentecostal church who contacted us too. Pastor Walt wanted us to visit his church and give our testimony.

It was an hour and a half drive. We got up earlier to start early. The girls were giving us trouble. The truck started to drive in jerks and spurts. Carburetor trouble. But we made it, a bit late.

We sang and gave a brief testimony.

"Have dinner with us," Pastor Walt insisted." We simply have to hear more of your testimony. And you have to sing for us again."

The roast was enhancing their home when we got there, and dinner was soon on the table. Dinner and an afternoon with them was something we don't want to forget. Pure unadulterated Christianity. They seemed totally confident in their humility because they had no veneer that needed to be polished. They both seemed broken and contrite before the Lord. Not ashamed to let a tear slide down a cheek if they were telling of what the Lord was doing for them. He was a big hardworking logger who was able to pastor a church, and she a total homemaker, who had totally lost herself in serving the Lord.

Even when we spent the afternoon riding their horses, they praised and praised the Lord. Especially, did I notice that.

"You know, Becky, you will receive the Baptism tonight." Rob told me on our way to church.

No way, I thought. This has been too big a day. I have a doozey of a headache and haven't had a cigarette all day. I have to get home and get to bed.

I deliberately hid out in the back room with the girls. I would have loved to hear Rob preach. He was preaching on Joshua 3 - crossing the River Jordan with the Arc of the Covenant. 'How can he think of a sermon just like that?' I wondered. We had been reading the same Bible.

As much as I wanted to hear that sermon, I didn't want to be in there. I didn't want to fall, like I'd seen some people do. I didn't want to make a fool of myself. I'd stay within the safety of the mother's room.

The door opened slowly as this huge man came in to sit down beside me.

"Becky, Rob has been telling me that you have not had the baptism. Why don't you come and join us and see what the Lord has in store for you tonight."

"Rob," I fumed inwardly, "how can you do this? How can you discuss my spiritual life with someone else, even if he is a minister?"

It was impossible to resent the quiet urging of this humble Christian beside me. I followed him with the children in tow.

If this thing is real ... great. If it isn't, I don't want anything to do with it. I don't want to make a fool of myself.

But I am tired of fighting.

As Rob called people forward, I came. I wanted total victory, like I had seen today. I wanted, above all, the spirit of praise.

I surrendered my will. My spirit melted before the Lord, and in that tiny, tiny church, before the most humble servants I had ever known, the spirit of praise caught my lips. My soul caught the fire from the glory that Christ had with the Father before the world was. I felt an explosion of praise that my vocabulary had no words for. So I talked with the tongue of angels. I lost my sense of time. I only wanted to cry out a praise that I had never known before. *His praise will always be on my lips.*

ROB

From Becky's lips flowed praise in song, in tongues. It was an expression of joy for the moment she was living.

I noticed that she lost the skeptic's hesitation about our endeavors here. She lost the craving for a cigarette. She also seemed to have lost the nagging resentment because her mother had been snatched from her.

"A garment of praise for a spirit of heaviness." I heard her singing the song when I was out in the yard or coming in the door. My beautiful wife was joyful.

"I've had a bear hug from God, Rob," she cried.

Her energy was boundless. Contagious. It seemed people wanted to catch a part of it. When the roads permitted, folks began coming out to see us. She invited everybody.

"Drop in," she'd tell the folks at church, "we'd love to have you."

And I was no longer buying her cigarettes. After her long fight to overcome, the craving left her. It had been replaced with joy.

We were singing again. Becky, especially, felt if we were honest about our lives, the Lord would allow us to serve. We had been asked to go on the choir tour. Our chore problem was instantly solved.

Dear, good, Connie knew how to milk and take care of cattle.

"I can do it," she insisted. " I know how to milk. And I also know how to clean barns. I wasn't a farm girl for nothing." She put an arm around Becky. "Go. Go. Let the Lord use your testimony."

Silver Lake in the Island Northwest was summer at its best. The dedicated youth ministers were an inspiration. Steve, the jolly, fun-loving Youth Director, and Steve Minton encouraged us, bolstered our confidence.

"You have wonderful rapport with the kids," they assured us over and over. We knew powerful prayer times. Young people were rededicated. We kept asking the Lord, "Can we be used of You, Lord? We know we have shady backgrounds. Can we actually be used?"

During our worship times at home, the question became part of our prayers.

Spring had run into summer, and I was still working at Pernsteiners to keep up with living expenses. Our bank account was down to about zero again, so our cattle were range grazing because we had no money for hay or feed. They were tame and came when we called and more often when we didn't call. There was new growth everywhere for them. They had enough to eat.

We were back to our working man's schedule with our morning routines abbreviated. Our mid-winter reprieve from scheduled work was a time we had treasured and looked forward to it next year.

I came home from work to start the chores and my pet wasn't there to meet me. Nor did she come when I called.

"Seen Emily?" I asked Becky.

"You mean she wasn't there to greet you?"

Becky ran out and leaned over our new porch rail to look around. Thoughts of mountain lions were always on our mind. We never heard of them attacking humans - but a cow? We wondered. Where was Emily? "Why don't you call again, Rob. She comes running when you call," Becky suggested as we started down the drive.

"Emily, Emily," I called. "Come Emily."

"Come Emily," I kept calling.

Finally I heard her crashing through the woods. Where in the world had she been that she came home so late?

When I milked her, I noticed that her abdomen seemed enlarged, but she had been eating, hadn't she? Must have had a good day.

I was uneasy the next morning and was anxious to check on her. What I found was worse than I feared.

"Oh God," I cried, "could she have bloated?" She was on her back with her feet extended on either side of her huge hard belly. Her eyes had rolled back, and I thought she was dead. But when I lifted her head she blinked. She was still alive.

"Becky! Becky! I think Emily has bloated!" I shouted as I ran for my black book and started running through the alphabet. 'Bloat,' I read, 'quickly poke a hose down her throat to her stomach to relieve the gas.'

"Did you hear that Becky? You have to help me. We may lose our cow!" I shouted.

I dashed for the garden hose and chopped off a piece. Becky ran to her side and was ready to help.

"Hold her head up, Becky. Up! Up!"

"Oh Rob!" cried my wife. "Oh Emily, you can't die on us! We need you so badly!"

"Up!" I ordered as I started pushing the hose over her bloated tongue and down her throat. Amazingly, it found its way to her stomach, and a volume of explosive gas and green vomitus was emitted.

"Oh Rob," Becky sobbed as she hugged our cow. "We can't lose her. We simply can't. Lord Jesus, You helped us out of so many troubles. Help us now with this cow. We need her so badly."

Emily raised her head and looked at us as though she understood that we were trying to help her.

"I think she's going to be alright." I was encouraged. She looked like she was going to make it, the big belly had decreased.

But she jerked, rolled back, and her eyes once more became glassy.

"I have to run for a vet Becky! Stay with her, honey. I'll be back."

I roared off down the hill with Brutus; I shouted to God. I was distraught, heartbroken. "God, I should have called a vet right away! But I had no money for a vet. What are You trying to do to us, God? Wring every drop of anguish out of our hearts?"

My old friend Brad met me. He was getting used to my wild flying hair. It must have looked familiar to him.

Anguished. It was about the only way he ever saw me. "My cow is dying, Brad. My cow is dying. I got to call the vet."

"Sure thing, friend," he said as he ran beside me to the house. "My goodness, that wasn't your cow that got into my feed? That little Jersey? Man, that's terrible. I thought it was one of mine that got out of the pasture and found the feed in the shed."

"Your shed! Whatever was she doing down here? She's never left our place before."

"She most likely came in heat. Cows do that. Take off running all ways at once. She must have gotten the door open and tanked out on the feed. Man, I'm real sorry about that!"

"Here," he said, as he poked the phone book at me. "Here's a good vet. He always comes on the double."

Our yard was soon astir with all the efforts to help.

"Looks pretty bad," the vet frowned his pronouncement. "I'll give her a shot. It just may work, but she looks pretty far gone."

Becky hid her face and cried.

Emily didn't stir from the needle, and she never did stir after that from anything.

"She's gone," said our doctor. He confirmed it with a stethoscope on her heart that would never beat again.

Becky collapsed to sob on her neck. I couldn't believe it. Gone? Just yesterday morning she gave us our pail of milk and now - she's gone?

Brad took charge. He called the shots in his most brusque style.

"Hook the chain on her, Son," he ordered as he put a foot on her head. "Gotta get her outa here. These folks won't know what to do with her."

I wanted so much to sock this good neighbor. Didn't he know he was stepping on her eye? Didn't he know how much we loved this cow? She wasn't just a dead cow. She was Emily, who left our little world very, very empty.

But he was right. We wouldn't for the world have known what to do with her. He and his son were saving us a very painful decision.

I sat on the tailgate of Brutus and cried. Ashamed that I cried, but I even sobbed as I cried. "I don't know where to go from here. And now we have a vet bill and no money to pay for it." I was telling these things to God so only He could hear.

"We loved her - we loved that cow, Lord, and we needed her so much. What would we do for milk? What would our little pigs do for milk? Don't You care about things like that?

"Does it matter to You God, that we try so hard to please You? Why? Why?"

Becky went in to put together a noon meal for us. She brought out the last quart of Emily's milk.

"How do we drink this?" I cried. "Isn't there some fitting ceremony for drinking the very last drop of milk from a cow who will never put milk on this table again?" It seemed a savage unfeeling thing to do. But because we needed it, we drank it. Becky thanked God for the joy Emily had given us and the good milk she had provided.

"I know You have something in store for us," she said humbly to her Lord.

I missed the nudge of my cow when I was looking under the hood of my truck. I missed her behind me when I carried in wood and when I hauled the water from the spring. I missed squirting her wonderful milk into the open mouths of our little pigs and watching them dance and jig so they wouldn't miss a drop of it ... She wasn't around the yard anymore and nothing seemed the same.

In two days we were due at the Christian Day Camp.

I can't go Becky! I just can't go to camp! How can I be a blessing to anybody when I feel like this? Maybe this is God's way of telling me that I am not fit for any kind of ministry. He wants me to stay out of that camp. Maybe that makes more sense than anything else I can think of."

"Maybe He wants to show You that He can turn this tragedy into something that will be a greater blessing than you can imagine." She put her cheek next to mine before sitting down to the table.

"Let's not talk about it, honey," she said as she grabbed my hand. "Let's just see what the Lord can do."

We went to camp.

I only confided to Steve D. I knew I looked disheartened and couldn't shake it. I felt I had to try and explain it.

But our songs seemed to be a blessing. Young people were filled with the Spirit. Once again Habakkuk became my guide. "The just shall live by faith." I couldn't understand it, I could just believe it; I couldn't leap like a deer, but we could sing.

Even as we started to sing the Spirit fell on the service. Young people were rededicating their lives at every meeting. And the Spirit fell on us too as we saw the work being done. We were awed by what was happening.

But we were without words and almost without breath to speak them at the last service.

We knew that there would be a collection for a ski boat for the camp. They had been talking about their need for it all through camp and had planned for it for months.

"Something has come up," Steve Minton told the teens at the last meeting we would have with them. Something has come up.

"Just before this meeting our friends, Rob and Becky, lost their pet cow. She wasn't only their pet cow -

they depended on this cow for milk for their family. Now they not only have lost their source of milk, but they also have a vet bill.

"Do you suppose we could help them?"

"Yes!" chorused the kids.

"Could we delay getting that ski boat for another year?"

"Yes! Yes!" they shouted.

"Let's give from our hearts. Rob and Becky need help - now. Let's help them with this very big loss."

When they passed the collection plate, the teenagers began giving. They heaped three hundred dollars on the collection plate and to that, our music director added a check for another hundred.

Once more we were melted before the Lord. Becky was able to thank them better than I was. But I did thank them, humbly, not only for the money that we needed so badly, but more than that - for the affirmation that we could be used of the Lord.

Chapter 20

BECKY

"Don't forget the assembling of yourselves together..." How could we do otherwise? We were back. We were at church on our spot of earth. Again we were embraced. We knew we were loved.

"Tell us something about your Silver Lake Bible Day Camp, Rob." Pastor Bowe leaned our way from the pulpit. "We've been hearing some very wonderful things about that camp."

Rob told about the stirring of hearts as the Holy Spirit fell on the young people of our camp. "Even when we were singing we could feel the moving presence of God," he said. He told how we had lost Emily two days before the camp and that we were wondering if, perhaps, the Lord didn't want to use us anymore.

"We were so broken before the Lord that when we witnessed the outpouring of love from the young people I could hardly express my thanks." He held hard to the pulpit as he measured his words. "And I hardly knew how to thank my Lord," he said as he looked past the window to the mountains where we were learning our lessons from God.

"Not only for the money that we needed, but more than that, for the affirmation that the Lord wanted us back singing again. That he could use us." It was all he was able to say.

Our little cabin looked inviting whenever we came home to it now ... almost as though it was holding out its arms. Our efforts were rewarding.

"Come up to our house," we told folks. "We'd love to have you."

Hazel and Carl drove up. Pushing seventy, they had lived our life and liked to talk about it. They had married during the Depression; they knew times without a job, mornings when you feared what the day had in store for you. They had carried water in a bucket, had an outside toilet, a boiler hanging on an outside wall. It was a step back for them to what they had known, and they acted as though they were among old friends.

Carl had an idea and couldn't wait to spring it on us. He didn't announce it, he just went out to his car, reached in the back and pulled out this large and unwieldy guitar.

"What you guys need is a guitar." Carl was excited. He patted its shiny strings as he mounted our steps. "Brings out a good beat in a song."

"You know, you have something there," Rob agreed. "I have a banjo in the shed. Why don't I play the banjo, and Becky, you know the cords. You're right, Carl. That was a great idea bringing us your guitar." He was on his way to the shed.

The guitar had a familiar feel as I threw the cord

around my neck. I think I surprised myself and Carl as I found the cords. It was a refresher course in something I had once been very excited about.

"Let's try something simple, Becky. How about something like, *'Power in the Blood.'* I love that old song," Carl suggested.

"Would you be free from your burden of sin
There's power in the blood."

It had been years since I sang that song. Now I had lived to learn something about that power. "That's the source of our miracle," I told them. "It changes lives. Seems we had to come up here to learn it. It's our miracle on the mountain."

Hazel didn't just sing. She worshipped as she sang. I knew she had found that power in her life. To me, it was like a discovery, singing the old songs again. Written during a time when the saints sang out about their salvation.

I made a quick mental note that it was not unlike enshrining on my walls what the pioneers had left behind of their struggle. Singing these old songs with Hazel and Carl was like finding a path marked by the niches of Christians who had little in life but the joy of their salvation.

"Leaning On The Everlasting Arms" we sang, with renewal fervor. *"Turn your eyes upon Jesus - Look full in His wonderful face - And the things of this world will grow strangely dim - in the light of His wonder and grace."* We remembered the times on our knees last winter, during our prayer times, when we had found everything we needed on our knees.

Then the kids started coming out to see us. Thirty

or forty of them at a time. The girls slept in sleeping bags in the cabin and the boys spread out in tents. We were not running a camp. They just came to visit. I cooked and cooked. The girls all helped. After breakfast they washed their hair. In buckets.

I was sure that Rob would get to think that he was some cool comedian. Every corny joke brought down the house. He kept the boys lugging water. After our cleanup work, we spread out for Bible study. Rob's mid-winter Bible study paid off. He was prepared. His theme never wore out. "Salvation becomes a process of obedience, self denial and perseverance. There are no shortcuts to character but the time proven methods." He had been reading the pamphlets written by Keith Green. There are no compromises.

And we sang with vigor and meaning. No neighbors came over to tell us to turn down the volume. We hiked through the mountains, and just to be sure the youngsters would work up an appetite for dinner, Rob reached back to the oldies for games. "Kick the Can" and "Hide and Seek".

From those starting life or ending it, the denominator for us was the same. He must increase and we must decrease. *His praise shall always be on our lips.*

ROB

Summer of '86 was the year we would tackle the Christmas tree project and make money. We knew how. We'd learned something from our Montana friend. We found we could rent 640 acres from the forest service on top of Stranger Mountain and cut trees for about 50 cents a tree. It would take about five hundred dollars.

I cut firewood during the summer to pay for leasing the acreage and was ready to start cutting all those trees. I set up a base camp about 5,000 feet up that mountain, put in a heater and practically lived there. Kept driving back to keep up the home front.

That's when I made a good friend. Joey Landon. He joined me on the mountain, and we worked good together. Young, eager, and wanting to serve the Lord, we didn't know at the time that we'd be working together for years to come. After a day in the woods, we'd sit around the stove to study our Bible and pray. Then we'd figure out our take on this thing. Expected to clear at least $10,000.00.

We cut trees together, hauled them to our lot and started selling. The first week one doesn't expect to sell many trees. Folks have to get in the mood.

We sold $2,200.00 worth of trees that week. Some trees went for $23.00. People loved those Alpines. Folks that bought them last year braked when they saw our sign and turned in. Maybe they had last year's decorations, handmade by the children and chuck full of memories and needed another ugly tree this year to hang them on.

It was a good hand rubbing time, which made one look around for a chance to spread the business. We needed another lot.

I didn't have the money to rent another lot, which cost about $600.00 and figured with the start-up costs it would amount to about a thousand. So I did what every enterprising businessman does who is worth his salt. When he sees a good thing - he borrows. I borrowed from Rick. The Rick who was part of the worship team that came to rescue us when Brutus was heading for the bottom of the canyon.

Why not try Douglas Fir? That way we could please them all. How could we lose? Not everyone caught the ugly-tree fever. There were a lot of conservative people that preferred the solid old Douglas Fir. Why not get that customer too?

I took all the money we had, rented a truck and drove a red eye stint to Seattle for Douglas Firs. Now I had to set up stands, set up lights, rent a camper, and do all the things it that it took to get another lot going.

We bombed. And we don't know why.

It was hard to take. My dream was to make a regular business out of Christmas trees. What better way to have free time for the ministry. Our mountain, our cabin, our church, we had everything we wanted from life. And we had free time for Bible Camps and our ministry in song. A bundle of hopes and dreams withered as we locked up and cleared our lots. By the time I paid Joey and the other workers, I dared to make only one mortgage payment!

And this was the time that Old Brutus decided that he'd had it. Every repairman agreed with him.

"I'm afraid you'd be throwing good money after bad." I didn't argue. But Brutus had found a place in our lives that made him hard to part with. We decided we would give him a spot with us not unlike the covered wagon that the oldsters used to enshrine in their yards.

But we had to have a car, so once again I walked my finger through the ads to find an old T-Bird we could get for $700.00. It eased our pain a bit, for it gave us the first sense of elegance we'd had for what seemed an awful long time. Whatever was under the hood, the lines of that

Thunderbird looked pretty slick.

I also slid a finger down to Help Wanted. Found an ad for work on the ski-lift, and that was the first destiny for our new car. I went out there and got the job.

Joey got a job up there too. P.J., the friend who helped me patch together our carpeting, was up there. He actually had been a carpet layer, but unemployment in our area ran about 30-40%. Nothing enhances one's skill-tank like that figure. One grabs whatever job is available and learns fast. I think the employers counted on us giving our jobs all we were worth. What we shared in common were cold winters and a hardy cold weather appetite. To eat, we had to work and work good.

Their clientele were an elite, almost sophisticated bunch, and a delight to work with. I wondered at the energy they put into a weekend, perhaps to compensate for a week of tensions at a desk. It confirmed my resolve that, right here, Becky and I had it all. These brilliant peaks around us that sparkle in the sunlight after the new snow decorates them almost every night - who wants the city? The flawless evergreens that seemed to spread their boughs for no other reason than to catch bunches of it, so the city folks would stand in wonder of it all - this is for us. Actually, for Becky and me, what people come for miles to enjoy, was our backyard.

And the natives around here - where else could you find folks like this? It seemed their only frills were how well they blended into the elements where they found themselves, with whatever earmarked their characteristics. Not afraid to be known as a 'character.' For the 'characters' up here enhanced our part of the world. Oh, I liked that.

Actually Joey, P.J. and I got to know each other

better working together here. They were dedicated and also wanted to find the deeper life in Christ Jesus.

It was a good time for us even though we didn't have the six month paid up security we had enjoyed the last two years from the Christmas tree sales. I was bringing home a paycheck, and we were making it.

And every year we became better friends of the youth pastor, Dan, and his wife Sandy. They always made us feel we were part of the team. "You know, Rob," Becky told me as we sat with our coffee around the heater stove as the skies were hurling their pellets at our windows. "Don and Sandy are about the most stable, faithful, reasonable people, I have ever gotten close to. They bow to God's will without question. Always. I want to do that."

"And she's such a good mother and housekeeper-" Becky continued as she covered the youngsters that were curled up like little kittens.

"What's the matter with you - ? They'd have to go some to out do you, honey."

"Well, she doesn't have to work at it as hard as I do. I wonder if being a nurse helps her be a better organizer," said my beautiful wife that I had begun to chalk-up as being practically perfect.

"Oh, you girls can rub off on each other. I heard her telling you that she wished she had your artistic touch."

When they joined us around our stove, we would talk about what was closest to our hearts. Youth work.

One night, as we sat together sipping hot chocolate and glancing out at the soft snowfall that was delighting us, Don laid it on the line.

"Have you ever thought about going into the ministry - full time, to work with youth?" Dan asked.

I choked a bit, because Steve Minton had asked me the same thing at Youth Camp. I looked out to the snowflakes as they dangled and played their way to our earth.

"I don't have the education, Dan." What a relief it was to say that!

Chapter 21

BECKY

Youth ministry? Possibly it was the weight of it that hung with me. It seemed constantly floating through my thoughts, like watching the moss on the trees when you're unsure of which way to turn.

For Rob, earning a living occupied him. Constantly. His promise to keep food on the table had no end in view. As the seasons changed, his skills had to adapt. And each new venture engrossed him totally.

"I'm learning, Becky. We used to call it 'job description' - how to get the job done. Here, every new job - we just dig in and do it, whichever way works best. Zane had the good recipe, "Hard work," he'd say, "just plain hard work, and keep at it 'til it's done."

He was still clutching for time so we could study and pray. The opportunities to sing and give our testimony kept coming, but Rob never felt completely ready for full time service. Not like we had graduated and were ready to be commissioned.

I felt we had something to say ... Every day seemed to bring a lesson that was preparing us. I was overcoming the bitterness in my life, and I felt I had learned something I wanted to share. I had found some answers that might help someone who was as desperate as I had been.

That's what youth ministry meant to me. An opportunity to spread some answers among the kids. The confused and hurt ones. I had learned what prayer can do. I had learned what surrender can do.

I had known the meaning of grief. I had felt the total depths of shame in a jail cell. I had known rejection. I had felt patience stretched until its threads were fraying. And now, His praise fell easier from my lips.

Nicotine had finally released its tentacles. There were fewer and fewer slammed doors during our days.

I felt more ready with an answer to Don's question. Yet I weighed the gravity of it. Because something lurked back there on the edges of *God's Design* that I felt should be dealt with. I found this hard to express to Rob.

I tried.

"Rob honey, I think there is someone who should know that we are considering a call to youth ministry."

Rob was fast falling asleep. I waited too long to get my question together. I waited too long to gather the courage. "Hmmm?" His head bobbed up from his pillow. "What'd you say Becky?" His eyes didn't open, they just struggled and flickered.

"Think about it, Rob..." I hesitated, lost my voice, fearful of letting the cork fly from a fermenting jug, I couldn't finish the thought.

"Think about what?" he muttered as he tried to come to. I knew he was too gone to deal with anything now, and I was relieved. I had lost my courage.

"Nothing," I said. "Go back to sleep." I brushed back his hair and slid over on my side of the bed. "You're too sleepy. We'll talk about it later."

"OK. Night."

I couldn't tell if my fears were reasonable, or was there a lingering hurt that I was unwilling to forgive? *It seemed he should settle with Rita that he wanted to live totally for the Lord and could never include her as a part of his life anymore.*

Was she still dreaming and hoping that her life would include Rob in it? I knew that Rob felt that because he knew it was over, she did also. But I never was sure.

Spring brought a job with Dan Dale the local landscaper. It was easier and more interesting than logging. Once again Rob was caught up in this new challenge. Transforming ugly spots into beauty. It was almost a story a day. And the pay-off was what happened to our own yard.

"Becky! We can do great things here. Get a load of dirt, some rocks and you can have a rock garden. We had shrubs left over from our last job. Some leftover gravel for a walkway. I learned that it takes a path to make an exciting garden design, Becky."

I was amazed to watch our moat of mud become a garden. The chickens and goats were fenced in now, and out of our yard.

Folks kept coming to visit us. The young people were in school, but we expected a mountain-full come summer and couldn't wait to surprise them. We had put a new face on our place.

But now it was spring and spring had her tricky little ways. One day it's balmy and the next day she flirts with old winter. That's when we found four inches of snow dumped on our yard.

We stayed home from church. It was muddy! Water all over!

The girls were running around in their pajamas. Rob was trying to quiet them down with the reindeer book. I was making hot chocolate. We could do fun things now like float marshmallows in it.

"A-stay-at-home-evening is a warmer for the heart, hon. This place does look so pretty." Rob looked up at me as he reached for Tasha's cup.

"I know, honey. I bet nights like this are times the kids will remember." We laughed at them. They each had decorated themselves with chocolate mustaches.

"Mama, can we sing with you before we go to bed? It's fun to watch you play that guitar. I like it a lot."

We sang "Climb, Climb Up Sunshine Mountain," and even sang some rounds.

"OK - time for bed," Rob ordered, and the girls danced to their cots. He tucked them in and pulled up the sheets after we listened to their prayers. They each had their own prayers. Anja was praying longer and longer prayers and Tasha, not to be outdone, made hers almost as long by repeating the ones she wanted to be blessed. We felt like good parents.

"Being we have the instruments out, let's practice a bit, Becky. Get in good voice for the choir tour."

"Rob, did you hear that Don's son Ron is coming out and will be at the church again soon?"

"Yeah, that's right. He knows how to get everybody to sing up a storm when he gets here. That guy really can sing and it seems he can play almost any instrument."

"Do you remember what church he is working

with, Rob?"

"A church in Vancouver ... let's see ... Glad Tidings I think."

We heard a knock on the door.

"Who in the world, Rob! Who could ever make it up our driveway through this mud?"

Rob got up and slowly inched his way to the door while trying to peer through the windows. It was black out there.

There was another knock. More urgent.

Rob pulled the door open slowly. We both gasped. Like in shock when your head feels drained while your feet can't move.

She was dripping. Muddy. Mud even dripped off her hands because she had fallen in it. Had she been drinking? She steadied herself on the screen door.

We were speechless.

"Oh, did - I - come - to - the - wrong - door? I could feel the shame of her predicament. She tried to make it less gross and salvage some poise. "I - got - some - friends - living - up - here."

"Come in, Rita," Rob said at last.

I offered her a cup of coffee. Rob offered her a chair.

"How are you kids making it?" she stammered.

Three years! It had been three years! Whatever made her pick a night like this for a visit? We're seventy miles from Spokane. How did she find out where we lived? My heart actually ached for her, and I blessed the ache. Did that mean I was able to forgive?

"Listen Rita." Rob was as serious as I'd ever seen him. "I wronged both you and Becky. It was a terrible, terrible sin. I can't tell you how sorry I am. God has been dealing with me, Rita." She was crying and so was I.

"I really have been wondering if God can ever use me in His work again. That sin seems to stand between me and a commitment to be used in the ministry. I'm so sorry, Rita. I'm sorry for my dear wife. I'm sorry for you. I don't feel I can even ask you to forgive me, the sin is so great."

She stood to leave.

"My car is stuck in the mud, Rob. Could you help me get it out?"

"Becky, can you come with me to the road to help Rita get out of the mud?"

I was torn between thinking she was scheming to get alone with Rob again and really needing help. How would he handle this? This was it. This was the real test. Had I been living a dream?

"The children are asleep, Rob."

"That's OK. Let's get some blankets on them and go together."

He carried a big girl, dangling arms and legs on either side of him. I carried Tasha. On that terrible cold and rainy night a family was walking out to complete a closure to a disruption in their walk before God ...

We didn't feel the darkness, the wind or the mud. As Rob pushed tree boughs under the tires, I felt, perhaps, I understood Rita. Rob had declared himself and his commitments. I understood how she must have felt, and it helped me understand myself. I gave her a hug.

When Rita was finally headed for home we felt ready! Set Free!

ROB

Morning didn't bring me the release that I noticed in Becky. She was singing while making kitchen noises, meaning that breakfast would soon be on the table.

I couldn't shake last night. I couldn't shake Rita. I finished the chores while my past clung to my thinking, something about the muddy tracks I used to leave behind me, sometimes without even knowing it.

Forgiveness didn't erase the consequences of my sin. Not when others were paying a price.

I remembered the rock skimming we had done as kids. The range of the ripples boosted our boast. We'd watch those rolls as they swelled out over the water. The ripples I had left behind had hurt. It didn't seem right that I should forget too easily.

My thinking affected the way I walked, the way I hung my mackinaw on the hook. I felt God's forgiveness, but my soul wasn't emblazoned by a new morning. I was bent. I was turning a bend in the road. I would, forevermore, walk with more awareness of the consequences of my steps.

"Honey, you haven't forgotten that Pastor Bowe asked us to sing, Sunday?" Becky called as I washed my hands for breakfast.

"That's right, he did." I meticulously rubbed each finger before looking up. Neither of us had said one word about the visit from Rita last night ...

"Have you given any thought to what we might sing, Rob?"

"We should keep a log of what we have sung, where, so we don't repeat ourselves."

"I know. We'll get to it, honey. How about the oldie that we sang at camp last summer, "The Blood Will Never Lose Its Power." No one has come up with a better cure-all. It sure moved the hearts of the kids there. You know, honey, more and more it seems we are tieing up the loose ends so the Lord can use us. Especially with kids. You really have a way with kids, Rob."

"A way with kids." I pondered over that statement, too, and didn't have much to say about her biscuits that I usually rave about. In fact, I didn't say much of anything and she noticed that.

"Rob honey, something is bothering you, isn't it? Is it about last night?"

Anja was about to scramble out of her chair to tackle the world outside that was becoming more spring-like every morning. Tasha had her mouth full and was squirming to follow her sister in the adventure.

"Yes, it is Becky. Give me a day or two to sort things out."

"I understand, Rob." There seemed much more she could have said, but nothing could equal the balm of, "I understand.'

The church was full and the congregation never opened up to sing to the rafters as we did when the pastor's son led the singing. Big, he still had the hearty look of having been nurtured by hearty breakfasts and the boisterous enthusiasm that everyone hoped he would never outgrow. It was contagious.

He took us through the praise choruses. It seemed even the older folks had learned to love them. Loved to raise their hands to sing their adoration directly to their Lord.

During the offertory Ron leaned over to us and

shook hands.

"Heard you're singing," he said.

I nodded.

"Great, I've heard about your singing, and I want to hear you."

We could see the Bowe's beaming at their son. Blonde like his father, he had the contagious spark of his mother.

We gathered together after the service with Ron and his wife. Ron was all energy and optimism.

"You know Rob," Ron enthused, "Dad has nothing but marvelous things to say about you and Becky and your work here with the teen-agers. Told me how the kids had been gathering at your place for Bible study and sleep overs."

"It's become our life here, Ron." Becky couldn't hide her eagerness, her longing to work with kids.

"Tell you what," Ron continued, "our pastor in Vancouver, Pastor Melin (we call him Bo) has dreams of what might be done with a ministry just for kids. You know what? I'm going to talk to him about you two and what you've been doing here."

I started at his suggestion. *Lord is this from you?* Suddenly the need of our mountain sanctuary was replaced by a longing to get into His work. Especially if it meant working with kids.

Was God really telling us that we could be used?

Chapter 22

BECKY

Waiting. Wondering. It made laying out the fleece seem a breeze. At least you would have your answer in the morning. Neither of us could turn off our thinking of what the will of the Lord was for us. It made us shift emotional gears often.

On misty mornings, Rob would call me outside. "Oh Becky, do you really think the Lord is calling us from all this? Look how those mists weave around the mountains. You know, we have it made right here. All this and our ministry too!" I had to agree with him. We had found a little wonderland for ourselves.

Then Hazel and Carl would come out with the kids on the weekends. Now there was even more purpose to our being together with this older couple. If we should ever be going into youth ministry full time ... What might we learn from them?

There was more listening. What could have been

just a happy conversational exchange between Christians doing something for the Lord, became a search for messages. What had they learned from experience-of-life that we could pass on? Pass on to youngsters torn from old family values and learning survival on the streets.

And from television where the most aggressive win.

Where the line between assertive and aggressive is never made very clear to young minds bent on survival. On the street, the smart answer becomes their most forceful tool and often their weapon.

"I'm learning from you, Hazel," I told her.

"Oh Becky, what are you learning? How to make sour dough biscuits?" she laughed.

"Well, that too! But I've been thinking about how God deals with the 'generation gap.' The difference doesn't seem to be the span of years between you and the kids ... it's the values these kids are handed. Didn't you have a better concept of what is right and wrong?"

"Well I hadn't thought of that."

"I mean 'selfish' used to be just plain bad. Now selfishness is in. It means good self image, good self esteem. You know, I find that hard to deal with. Rob and I have been singing '*More holiness give me,*' and I just don't find selfishness in any of the answers we find, Hazel."

"You know something, Becky. You never will. I know the Lord has a place for you in full time youth ministry. We'll just have to wait."

ROB

Waiting is no spiritual retreat. I had to figure how to keep the paycheck coming in so our winter needs would be met. It was easier now that I had learned how to shift with the season.

I had learned the value of old Zane's advice. "Well now," he'd say, "this be the time that we head back into the woods. That's where the money's at."

So I was back logging, and I liked it. Christmas trees would come later, like the alternate plan.

I had made arrangements for the Choir Tour. Mom and Dad would be taking care of the kids. Becky and Mom had developed a deep admiration for each other. Mom rejoiced that we had gotten our lives together with the Lord, and Becky appreciated how unselfish Mom was, always there to help. The goats were milking again and Connie would be coming to care for the animals.

The Choir Tours were always exhilarating. Happy, exuberant people traveling together, singing together, had found a way to be used of the Lord. It seemed Becky and I were singing better and better together.

Word got around that Pastor Bo might be meeting us on this trip, so everyone waited with us. Even prayed with us. The pull of our mountain and the pull of Youth Ministry became our tug-of-war, and it came without the fleece that Becky often talked about.

When we were singing in Mosseyrock, the pastor there, got the word that we were awaiting a possible call from the Glad Tidings Church in Vancouver.

"Why, we could use you in Mosseyrock for our young people. See that little place over there? We could even set you up with a house so you two could move right in."

How wonderful it was to be needed. But we had to wait for a word from Bo.

Pastor Melin met us and shared his dreams of a youth ministry just for teenagers. He made us aware of the responsibility that comes with such an undertaking.

"Can I set you up for an interview with our church board?" he asked as he rose to leave. "They will want to meet you." For both Becky and me, it seemed our turn in the road would be determined by what they thought of us in Vancouver. We knew the mountain was losing out. We were ready to go.

But no request such as that was without its bundle of jitters. We felt we had been schooled with the right answers; but had the mountain rusted our company manners? We found ourselves wanting so much to be approved. We hoped it wouldn't be a long wait.

That evening Becky gave me the news. She was pregnant.

Chapter 23

BECKY

Hot showers at the Red Lion, or if you choose ... you might soak in the perfumed waters of a mammoth tub. Our suite seemed very elegant. Perhaps many people were awed by the luxury of it all, but none more than we. We had truly forgotten that people lived like this.

Our pastor and his wife drove us to Vancouver. Mavis knew how morning sickness felt, and no mother could have been more solicitous.

"Eat crackers, honey. It really does help. Oh, we're so happy and proud of the two of you."

"They haven't given us the thumbs up yet," Rob rejoined.

"Wait 'til they hear you two sing," Pastor Bowe said confidently.

Sing? Oh I hope the crackers will help.

Everything, even the parking lot of the Glad Tidings Church, seemed to come in great proportions as compared to our little church in Addy. The sanctuary, with its balcony and the huge sliding doors that instantly made the church larger when they were pushed opened, seemed overwhelming. We had been meeting in a gym for so long we had forgotten there was any other way.

The congregation seemed especially large when I learned that Rob would be preaching to that crowd Sunday night. Pastor Melin had announced in church that Rob would have the Sunday evening service. He wanted the church to meet us.

I felt sicker than I wanted to admit. How does a mother handle morning sickness at a time like this? The congregation was so loving and warm that I was sure they would understand, but who was going to tell them?

Did I show? We didn't have money for new clothes, and my curtain dress was looking very tight. I found a black dress at a thrift shop with a lacy top. It looked very nice, and Rob assured me that no one would ever guess. Especially if I faced directly front.

Facing front is not the way I usually sing, but I did that night. Both Rob and I prayed that I wouldn't toss my last meal. I ate crackers and we sang *'The Blood Will Never Lose Its Power.'* I don't believe we ever sang it better.

"You were wonderful," Mavis leaned over to whisper to me. Rob preached on James 1 - The value of trials and struggles in preparing the heart of the child of God. I drank in his words, for I had witnessed the change in this man. I had seen his struggle to overcome. Knew of his struggle to find time to search the scriptures. Heard his cry for holiness. I also remembered him jamming his hands in his mackinaw so Zane wouldn't see how soft they were. Now his preaching hand was hard and calloused like a lumberjack's. I wondered if anyone noticed that.

They found us a beautiful home right next to the

church. We felt we had been received into the hearts of these wonderful people. We felt the will of God.

Rob agreed to begin there in two weeks.

ROB

We headed down our drive with both fervor and homesickness. What we had claimed - we were leaving. What we had learned - we were committing. Youth work ... we felt compelled to embrace it.

This last trip down our drive wasn't a - "Vancouver, here we come" - experience at all.

The pine was still as pungent; it had helped in the healing. We were aware of that. The curves had slippery spots in the winter that I wouldn't forget, where I would spill water while struggling over the ice. Our goats and hens had scared each other into such a pandemonium, and raised such a hullabaloo of racket, that we wondered if the echoes on our mountain weren't vibrating yet. Emily took off down this drive for an adventure that took her from us. We had started off down this drive the Sunday morning that brought us within inches from tumbling into the valley beneath us.

It was a head-bowing pause for an unexpressed prayer. We took each other's hands. A moment like this is not unlike the solemnity of marriage.

We looked back to our spot of earth. The spot made beautiful by our efforts. I remembered that I had promised Becky I'd fix up that little place. Petunias were cascading over the porch. Grass was growing where grass should be. The mountains were still weaving across our sky as though hanging in the mists. It was October. It had been a long wait.

It was a spot that had heard our prayers and our cries. It had become our sanctuary and our seminary. God had not given us a spiritual hammock. We each bowed in reverence of what we had learned there.

Two weeks to move. We were glad we had a short time frame. Our place had sold quickly with no problem. We had taken our goose, our chickens and our goats to the Grange; they had promised to find a good home for our animals. We couldn't leave Brutus and we couldn't take him with us. He could still break trail through the snow-drifts that pile up in this country. When we looked back at him standing on the lot where we left him, we thought he looked proud. He had helped us.

Packing had only taken a day's worth of effort. We had brought little with us and took little out. Our foam cushioned Costco couch would have to be replaced, but we couldn't part with it yet. Everything we took fit into the U-Haul driven by Dan Dale the landscaper, and into our little travel trailer that we were pulling behind the Thunderbird.

We had said good-bye to Brad.

"Greenhorn, you mean you're leaving us for those city slickers in Vancouver? You've barely got decent callouses on those hands of yours."

"Brad, how can I thank you for the many times you've pulled me out of a bind?"

"You know something, Rob and Becky, we're going to miss you. I don't think this mountain will ever be the same."

It seems mountain people grow to feel that way about each other.

The church had gathered like a family for our send

off. I had preached that morning on Ephesians 2:10 - *"For we are His workmanship, created in Christ Jesus unto good works, which God hath before ordained that we should walk in them."* With a commandment from the Lord like that, there seemed little that a sermon could add. I affirmed its call on our lives.

The ladies teased Becky during the potluck.

"Becky, we'll miss your curtain dress."

"Well, it's getting kind of tight. Besides, I didn't see anyone wearing a curtain dress in Vancouver."

Zane and Connie were among the first with their good-byes.

"If you give this thing your best shot like you did splitting that timber out in them woods thar, you'll do all right, friend."

"Connie," Becky cried on her shoulder, "do you realize how much you contributed to all this? How can we ever thank you?"

"Keep singing and praising the Lord," Connie said tearfully.

Parting from Hazel and Carl was difficult. We thanked them over and over for the guitar. "And for those old songs you folks sang with us. We might never have reached for those deep messages without those songs," Becky told them.

Becky clung to Dan and Sandy Stone. "We can't tell you what a role model you've been to us."

"Role model?" They both laughed together. Someday we'd tell them better what we meant by that ...

We missed Joey Landon. He was on a mission trip to Mexico. We had worked together like true brothers in the Lord.

The girls caught the thrill of a new venture. They

giggled when folks teased them about going to the big city.

We had wrapped it up and were leaving it all.

We wondered if we could ever replace folks like these. Folks we could laugh with, because at times things are funnier here. And folks we could cry with, because here life sometimes seems to hurt a whole lot more.

This driving off was ours to share with no one. We remembered our High School processional. Those notes - it seemed we could hear those notes once again. This time God's seminary doors had opened. We had been commissioned.

Epilogue

ROB

1993 - We just finished a Thanksgiving dinner with the 300 folks who joined us in worship this morning. Folks who have been painting our church and polishing it's pews. Our beautiful old edifice at the Corner of Sixth and Alberta has a bell tower that will never let you drive by without noticing our name. *Portland Metro* is in the very heart of Portland.

We have been here two months.

It has been a journey of awe and gratitude since we drove off our mountain six years ago. Gratitude to Pastor Melin, who pushed us right into his dream of a ministry for youth.

We found the spot for that ministry in a remodeled warehouse on 18th Street in Vancouver. A place that could hold the kids that began coming, first in trickles but soon filling all the chairs we could crowd in there. That's when we noticed a problem.

These kids had problems. Drugs and alcohol, and with that, switch blades and anger.

They came from broken homes. I noticed that they had no recall of an old gospel song, or a homespun caution of sin. When we talked of a new life in Christ Jesus they had no idea of what that new life would be.

We were not starting from scratch. We were starting from tangle. We were starting with a young person, whose idea of right and wrong was only what worked for them, whose emotions were tangled by drugs and by what they had learned on the street.

It was almost five years after beginning our youth ministry at Glad Tidings church that we felt God wanted us to move our ministry into the heart of the inner city of Portland where we could also reach out for the parents of youth.

We began in a school gym while we searched for a better facility. It seemed a long search but we did find it here on Sixth and Alberta. We found this grand old church that was crying for our paint, our polish, and our prayers.

Today our sanctuary was filled with heartfelt awe of what the Lord has done.

BECKY

Our baby was a boy who looks and acts like his father. At two, Levi's drums were finding a beat for the gospel hymns as well as the choruses.

And then we had Reyna. She now is three, beautiful and amazingly obedient. It helps when her mother is so involved with our ministry.

Much of that ministry involves our young women and mothers. Because I too, had problems, it gives understanding of just what may be helpful to young women and mothers. So we deal with divorce and with those who have remarried. We have found books that help us in dealing with alcohol and drug dependency, eating disorders, and relationship problems. We also have a Bible study, and just recently started a Senior Ministry.

We still feel we are two workman that the Lord has to hone until we become more and more useable in the mission field he gave us. Every day we pray for that.

We have told our story as we remember it. It is a true story. We changed some of the names and our writer rearranged the sequence of a few events to enhance the story flow.

What we learned on our mountain we look back too, every day, as the seminary God prepared just for us. We draw from it. We learned, that come what may, we must arrange our day, so we can pray.

Ruth Smith

Strange, how we found each other. I had young people helping me with my acres who kept asking, "Have you ever heard of Rob and Becky? Have you heard of Club Revelations?

Then The Columbian devoted a full page featuring their work with Vancouver youth. I had to meet them.

The place was packed out. I stood singing without a songbook, the only older person in that congregation where the whole structure seemed vibrating with, "My hope is in you, Lord, In you. It's in you."

Then I stood transfixed, as I watched cigarettes being tossed on the alter, saw switch blades land up there too. These kids meant business. They wanted their lives changed.

Characteristic of Rob and Becky, they came to meet me. Wanted to know why I came. I told them that I write a bit, and this would make a good article.

"You write!" Becky cried. "What do you write?"

I bragged. I told them that I had won the very prestigious award, *The Moody Award For Excellence in Christian Writing* and along with publishing in nursing journals my winning story was published in The Decision Magazine. Now, I told them, I'm working on *Move On Prairie Preacher,* the experiences of weathering The Depression after my father's church had closed.

"I want to read that!" Rob said. "I want to read what you've been writing."

"I can't believe it," he said, as he handed my manuscripts back to me. "How our experiences paralleled each other. You had crazy goats, you lost your pet cow, were lost in a snow storm and arrived at a stinky house. I sure like what you write."

"Will you write our book?" Becky asked.

And just like that I said I'd love to. That was almost three years ago.

As you can imagine, we became family. I found them the warmest, hard working, dedicated Christians I've ever met.

I want to thank my sons for finding the flaws, and the endless patience of my daughter-in-law. My critique group for reading and rereading the rewrites. Especially, Rosie Jones, Louis Delano, Shirley Cooper, Carol Ahola and her daughter, April.